THE
COMPARATIVE PHYSIOLOGY
OF
RESPIRATORY MECHANISMS

THE

COMPARATIVE PHYSIOLOGY

OF

RESPIRATORY MECHANISMS

By

August Krogh

UNIVERSITY OF PENNSYLVANIA PRESS

Philadelphia

Printed and Bound in the United States of America by
Book Craftsmen Associates Inc., New York

PREFACE

The volume here presented contains the substance of the series of lectures delivered at Swarthmore in the spring of 1939, but a careful revision has been made and the text has in several places been amplified and added to. The manuscript was completed within that year, but the difficulties of communication have delayed publication and thrown a great burden of proofreading, correction, revision of literature, and preparation of name lists and general index upon my friends at Swarthmore and elsewhere. I am deeply grateful to Dr. Laurence Irving, Dr. Per F. Scholander, Dr. Edgar C. Black, and Miss Louise Boyden for the pains they have taken, and I desire also to express my appreciation of the splendid work done by the University of Pennsylvania Press under very trying circumstances.

As I have had an opportunity of going over the page proofs, I am personally fully responsible for the errors and omissions which no doubt remain.

AUGUST KROGH

THE LABORATORY OF ZOOPHYSIOLOGY,
COPENHAGEN UNIVERSITY,
October, 1940

CONTENTS

INTRODUCTION

THE phenomena covered by the word "respiration" are very diverse. When a person is seen to breathe, what is observed is a movement of the chest and abdomen by which air is alternately drawn into his lungs and again expelled. This constitutes the mechanical aspect of respiration. In man the mechanical breathing is essential to life, and it is one of the old tests for death to see whether these movements have ceased completely. In very cold weather it can be directly seen that the air expired contains a considerable amount of moisture above that present in the inspired air, and gas analysis reveals the fact that it contains less oxygen and more carbon dioxide. The absorption of oxygen into the lungs and blood, and the elimination of a similar amount of carbon dioxide constitute the physico-chemical aspect of respiration. A comparison of the venous blood entering the lungs with the arterial blood leaving them combined with a determination of the rate of flow shows that the oxygen removed from the air in the lungs is transferred to the blood and distributed to the tissues where some of it disappears and is replaced by CO_2 and H_2O. This "internal respiration" is the essential process, liberating energy like the burning up outside the organism of coal or any suitable organic material, but with the essential difference that while combustion processes outside an organism are generally limited by the supply of combustible material and oxygen they are within the body regulated, so as to supply the needs of the organism, and largely independent both of the supply of material and of the quantity of oxygen offered, provided this quantity is sufficient to meet the demand (Pflüger, 1872).

Within each cell the demand varies with the activity of that cell, and the demand of the organism taken as a whole also

1

varies with the activity, being at a minimum during complete
rest. In many organisms, including man, the mechanical
respiration and the circulation of the blood are "regulated"
so as to correspond to the demand of the moment.

In the present monograph we will not attempt to deal with
all the various aspects of respiration. The processes involved
in the internal respiration and their regulation will be taken
for granted, and the nervous and chemical mechanisms by
which the supply of oxygen to the tissues is regulated will be
considered only incidentally.

What I shall endeavour to illustrate is:

(1) the enormous differences in the "call for oxygen" shown by
    different organisms and under varying conditions;
(2) the variations in the accessibility of oxygen in the different
    habitats occupied by animals; and the main theme will be
(3) the adaptation of respiratory mechanisms to these widely varying
    conditions.

A description of adaptation can be arranged according to
the general zoölogical system, and I admit that for many
purposes such an arrangement is desirable, but as it turns out
that within the same systematic group we may have many
different types of respiratory organs I have tried to adopt a
physiological or œcological system, describing first the respiration of animals obtaining their oxygen from water by means
of organs of increasing complexity, culminating in the gills of
fishes. In the air-breathing animals the development of
lungs is followed up to their culmination in mammals and
birds. The respiratory functions of the blood in a number
of forms are discussed in a separate chapter, and finally the
tracheal respiration is discussed, by which oxygen is carried
directly to the respiring cells without the intervention of a
circulating fluid.

I

THE CALL FOR OXYGEN

TABLE 1 gives a summary of determinations of the metabolism as expressed by the amount of oxygen actually used per unit time and weight and at an outside temperature of 20°C. by a small number of organisms selected for the purpose of illustration. It shows, as one would expect, that size has a

TABLE 1

	Weight	Oxygen consumption ml/kg/hour
Paramœcium	0.001 mg	500
Mussel (*Mytilus*)	25 g	22
Crayfish (*Astacus*)	32 g	47
Butterfly (*Vanessa*)	0.3 g	
resting		600
flying		100,000
Carp (*Cyprinus*)	200 g	100
Pike (*Esox*)	200 g	350
Mouse	20 g	
resting		2,500
running		20,000
Man	70 kg	
resting		200
maximal work		4,000

considerable influence upon the requirements, but is not everything, since animals of the same weight may use very different amounts. It indicates further a very large effect of activity. We will try to analyse the factors influencing metabolism one by one.

The influence of size. By a study of dogs of different size, the oxygen intakes of which were measured under comparable

3

conditions of almost complete rest, constant temperature and so on, Rubner (1883) found that the metabolism was not simply proportional to the weight, but very nearly to $W^{2/3}$, the square of the cube root of the weight, which represents

TABLE 2

RESPIRATORY EXCHANGE OF WARM-BLOODED ANIMALS

	Weight kg	O₂/kg/hour ml	O₂/m²/hour liter
Horse	440	98	8.5
Pig	130	166	9.3
Man	65	280	9.1
Dog	15	450	9.0
Rabbit	2.3	650	6.8
Goose	3.5	580	8.8
Hen	2.0	810	8.8

TABLE 3

AVERAGE RESPIRATORY EXCHANGE OF GROUPS OF FOREST-SOIL ANIMALS AT $13°C$.

		Weight range mg	Average weight mg W	O₂/individual/hour/mg R	O₂/g/hour $\dfrac{1000\,R}{w}$ mg	O₂/surface unit/hour $\dfrac{100\,R}{\sqrt[3]{w^2}}$ mg
Worms.	Insects	1,211–277	755	0.118	0.177	0.149
Insects.	1 worm	271–94	186	0.047	0.260	0.145
Insects.	1 spider	84–15	40	0.0173	0.494	0.152
Insects		8.3–2.5	5.1	0.0037	0.731	0.123
Insects		2.2–1.2	1.7	0.0016	0.981	0.114

more or less closely the external surface. This comparison can be extended without encountering serious discrepancies to a considerable number of warm-blooded animals, as shown in Table 2, and for a long time it was thought that it expressed the conditions for heat loss which in a warm-blooded animal must be definitely related to the metabolism during rest.

Later it has been found, however, that also in cold-blooded animals a similar relationship between weight and metabolism holds good, and it is therefore probably of a much more fundamental nature. An illustration is given in Table 3 from determinations by Bornebusch (1930) on the animals living in forest soil.

The influence of organization. Many deviations from the weight-metabolism relation sketched above become apparent when different animals are compared—at a constant temperature and during rest—but the majority can be explained as due to differences in organization. Nobody would expect two animals of the same live weight, but having respectively 1/2 and 20% dry substance, like a jelly-fish and a cuttle-fish, to show the same rate of metabolism. Since a variable proportion of the dry substance may also be inactive, a better basis for comparison is the content of organic nitrogen, and many large deviations from the 2/3 power weight relationship disappear or become greatly reduced when comparisons are made on this basis, but some remain, and we have to admit as a fact that the metabolism during rest stands in a certain relation to the habitual activity of an animal, sluggish forms having a lower metabolism than active ones. Cases in point are the mussels *Cardium* and *Pecten* according to Spärck (1936), the fishes *Cyprinus* and *Esox* as shown in Table 1 and the reptiles *Anguis* and *Lacerta*.

The influence of temperature. The metabolism at rest is in all animals a definite function of the body temperature. This is true also for the warm-blooded animals, which habitually maintain by regulation processes a more or less constant body temperature, and it can be demonstrated when the body temperature is altered artificially.

The relation between temperature and metabolism can be expressed in the form of a curve, and such a curve, valid at least approximately for animals belonging to very different

groups, is shown in Fig. 1.   In several cases the increase in
metabolism with temperature is even larger than expressed
by this curve.

When studied at increasing temperature the metabolism
will be found to increase according to the individual curve

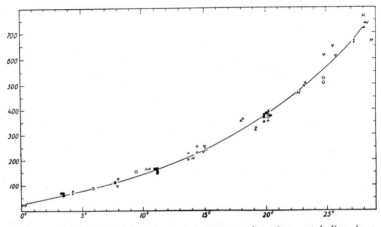

Fig. 1.   The relation between temperature and resting metabolism in a
frog, toad, goldfish, mosquito and a young dog.   Ordinate in arbitrary units.
(Krogh.)

only up to a certain point.   Beyond that there is usually only
a slight further increase and then a definite irreversible drop,
indicating that the high temperature is harmful and rapidly
fatal.

The influence of activity.   The effects on the call for oxygen
so far discussed are from the point of view of the efficiency of
respiratory organs of secondary importance only, because they
affect the minimum requirements, and the respiratory organs
must be able to meet the maximum requirements during
activity.   These requirements are not known, even approximately, except in a small number of cases.

We can state generally that the possible rate of sustained
activity stands in some relation to the body temperature.
This is common knowledge as regards, for instance, flies or

snakes, but recent investigations (M. Nielsen 1936) have shown that even in warm-blooded man muscular activity is correlated with a definite increase in temperature which normally reaches 39.5°C. (103°F.) when the metabolism is at the maximum of about 20 times the resting value.

It is important to note that it is the rate of activity that can be sustained over a certain length of time which determines the demands upon the respiratory organs. The oxidative processes are in the main processes of restitution which can be postponed for a certain length of time while the organism is incurring an "oxygen debt," to be paid off after the burst of activity. When activity is sustained a "steady state" is reached—in man after about 3–5 minutes—in which the oxygen intake has ceased to rise and remains more or less constant, corresponding to the rate of activity. In man and also in the horse (Brody and Cunningham, 1936) the maximum oxygen uptake to be provided by the lungs in such steady states of muscular activity is of the order of 10 to 15 or even in some individuals 20 times the resting metabolism.

In flying animals the maximum rate of oxygen uptake is much higher, as indicated by the figure given for a flying butterfly in Table 1.

The influence of adverse conditions. In the warm-blooded animals complete rest in a starving condition is characterized by a definite level of metabolism called the "standard" or "basal." It is important to note that in many cold-blooded animals there is no such well-defined basal level. If food is withheld the metabolism goes on decreasing, sometimes for very long periods, until death supervenes (Tetens Nielsen, 1935, and unpublished observations by the writer on several insects). The same takes place in other adverse conditions, and there can be no doubt that also lack of oxygen is a factor which can in many forms reduce the metabolism without appreciable damage to the organism. When, for instance, respiratory organs are removed by operation in May-fly larvæ (Morgan and Grierson, 1932) the respiratory exchange is definitely reduced.   At high temperatures this reduction is fatal, but in winter the operated animals live on and pupate normally.   Similarly Zoond (1931) has found that the branchial filaments of the sabellid worm *Bispira voluticornis* could be removed without injuring the animal's life, although the oxygen consumption would be reduced from 56 to 20 ml/kg/ hour.   K. Berg (1938) finds that the larvæ of *Chironomus liebelibathophilus* grow much more slowly at depths of 17–20 m in Esrom Lake, where the oxygen concentration is very low, than at 11–14 m where it is generally ample.

As matters stand at present there would appear to be three possible ways for animals to react to an inadequate supply of oxygen.   One is a simple reduction of requirements by slowing down vital processes, another is represented by incomplete oxidations, corresponding to an oxygen debt which is paid off when oxygen again becomes available, and the third is the definite transition to anaërobic metabolism by which comparatively small amounts of energy are acquired by the breakdown of large amounts of nutritive material and the products of this breakdown eliminated.   Harnisch (1937) has shown that both in true anaërobionts (*Ascaris*) and in free living forms exposed to lack of oxygen (*Tubifex, Planaria, Chironomus*) the products of anaërobiosis are oxidized within the body when oxygen becomes available.   This "secondary oxybiosis" is governed by oxidative enzymes in the hæmolymph, and its rate is clearly dependent upon oxygen concentration.

II

THE ACCESS TO OXYGEN

In nature we find animals in all kinds of environments where oxygen may sometimes be quite difficult to obtain and where the concentration of carbon dioxide may rise so as to seriously obstruct the elimination of this product of metabolism. It will be convenient to give at this stage a brief survey of œcological conditions so far as the respiratory gases are concerned.

The access to oxygen in air. The composition of the atmosphere is constant and can be taken as 20.948% O_2 and 0.030% CO_2 (Krogh, 1919) while the rest is a mixture of gases—inert from our point of view—and lumped together as nitrogen which in reality makes up about 78% while 0.94% is argon.

The changes in composition caused by respiratory or combustion processes are astonishingly small. In the streets of a large city the CO_2 may rise to 0.04 and the O_2 be lowered by a corresponding amount, and even in crowded rooms the changes are usually within 0.1% and practically always within 1%. They have no effect upon man or any air-breathing animal.

At the normal sea level barometric pressure of 760 mm mercury, the oxygen pressure corresponds to about 155 mm with small variations due to the varying content of water vapour. At higher altitudes the composition remains unaltered, but the pressure drops and at a height of 5000 m (= 16,000 feet) the oxygen pressure is 88 mm, which seriously affects the power of man and most warm-blooded animals to obtain the necessary oxygen from the atmosphere and strictly limits the ability to do muscular work.

Because the total pressure is variable it may be misleading to express the concentration of a gas in per cent of the atmosphere and in the following discussion concentrations will generally be given in mm pressure of mercury.

In the surface layers of the soil the increase in pressure is insignificant, but oxidative processes both inorganic and organic are at work by which O_2 is used up and sometimes CO_2 produced. Normally, however, the exchange with the free atmosphere taking place by diffusion and by barometric pressure variations is so considerable that the air differs only slightly from the atmospheric. Ege (1916) found in a forest 30 cm below the surface 0.2% CO_2 and 20.6% O_2, corresponding to pressures of 1.5 and 152 mm respectively. In a field the O_2 pressure was 153, in an anthill 145 and in a decaying beech trunk 133 mm. Portier and Duval (1929) found CO_2 pressures up to 14 mm in anthills in summer when the temperature was also several degrees higher than in the earth in the neighborhood. Fairly heavy rain will sometimes clog the pores of the surface so as to seriously reduce the exchange, and in one case Ege observed 30 cm below the surface in a field after rain the compositions and pressures given in Table 4.

TABLE 4

	mm pressure	
	CO_2	O_2
Field 30 cm depth	1.5	153
Same 6 hours after rain	46	64
" 11½ " " "	21	46
" 36 " " "	17	129

In such circumstances some of the animals living in the earth are apt to suffer and the earthworms may react by coming to the surface.

At greater depths, where only man will penetrate, the peculiar conditions first studied by Haldane sometimes give rise to serious accidents. Inorganic oxidative processes which do not give rise to any production of CO_2 take place regularly, but generally at a slow rate. The air is renewed mainly by the variations in barometric pressure, and usually this is sufficient to keep it respirable. When, however, water-bearing strata are cut off from the surface by an impermeable layer the air in such strata may be completely deprived of oxygen, and when a well is carried down into such strata it may be perfectly safe to work in it so long as the barometer is rising and air flows in, but extremely dangerous when the occluded air flows out by a falling barometer. A certain number of accidents, usually ascribed to "poisonous" gases, but simply due to lack of oxygen, are brought about in this way (Haldane, 1922).

Many animals live inside plants. In the few cases examined the air in plant tissues has been found to be perfectly respirable. In the roots and rhizomes of aquatic plants the oxygen pressure is, however, often greatly reduced. Figures as low as 15 mm O_2 in the summer and even down to 4 mm in winter were observed by Ege. On the other hand the assimilation of green submerged plants liberates free oxygen, and the bubbles which collect from them under ice may contain up to 45% O_2. Such air is utilized by several animals.

The access to oxygen in natural waters. Gases are soluble in water. When air-free water is in contact with an atmosphere consisting of one single gas the water will absorb that gas until equilibrium is established. The absorption coefficient is defined as the quantity of a gas, measured dry in volume units at one atm. pressure and 0°C, taken up by one volume of water from an atmosphere of that gas at normal pressure (760 mm). I prefer to express the absorption coefficient in per cent of the water volume. The absorption coefficient varies with temperature, and at a temperature of 15°C. we have for oxygen in pure water an absorption coefficient of 3.5%, for nitrogen 1.7%, and for CO_2 about 100%.

The quantity of any gas absorbed is proportional to the pressure of that gas and independent of any other gas that may be present. From the atmosphere O_2 and N_2 are absorbed simultaneously and independently, each according to its own pressure, and therefore in 100 volumes of water $\frac{155}{760} \times 3.5 = 0.72$ volume of O_2 and $\frac{605}{760} \times 1.7 = 1.35$ volumes of N_2.

Gases are somewhat less soluble in salt solutions, and Table 5 gives the quantities of O_2 in equilibrium with the atmosphere at different temperatures and salinities; $20^0/_{00}$ Cl corresponds to ocean water.

TABLE 5

OXYGEN IN FRESH AND SALT WATER SATURATED WITH ATMOSPHERIC AIR
ml/liter

	0	10	$20^0/_{00}$ Cl
0°C.	10.29	9.13	7.97
10°C.	8.02	7.19	6.35
15°C.	7.22	6.50	5.79
20°C.	6.57	5.95	5.31
30°C.	5.57	5.01	4.46

Compared with air the quantities of oxygen available in water are very small and for water in equilibrium with the atmosphere they vary with temperature. It is often desirable to express the concentration of a dissolved gas by its pressure in the atmosphere with which it would be in equilibrium. For this purpose we shall use the word "tension" to distinguish it from the actual gas pressure with which it would be in equilibrium. Tensions are given in mm pressure of mercury.

The oxygen in natural waters is mainly derived from the atmosphere and is taken up at the surface where the tension reaches 155 mm. It is transported downwards by diffusion (the movement of individual molecules) and by convection along with the water in which it is dissolved. Over distances above a few mm diffusion is a slow process, and it has been figured out for instance that by diffusion from the surface the first oxygen molecules would reach a depth of 250 m in 42 years.   If no oxygen was used up all waters would nevertheless have become fully saturated by diffusion.

Convection takes place to a large extent by currents generated by the wind, but temperature variations are also an important source of convection because of their effect upon the specific gravity of water.   Fresh water shows a maximum specific gravity at 4°C.   The presence of dissolved salts lowers the temperature of maximum density.   In brackish water of 18.6$^0/_{00}$ salinity the maximum is at 0°C, and in ocean water at − 3.5°.

In temperate regions the temperature of lakes will approach 4° during some period in the spring and the wind will usually cause the whole body of water to become mixed, but in the summer the upper layers of water are heated by day while the surface itself is cooled at night by evaporation and irradiation.   This causes a vertical convection down to a certain level, called the thermocline, depending upon the nightly cooling and the exposure to strong winds—say between 10 and 20 m—above which the water is regularly kept mixed and reaches during summer a fairly high temperature.   Below the thermocline the water is stagnant and the temperature remains low.

The influence of organic processes on the oxygen content of natural waters.   While in air the processes of assimilation and respiratory metabolism have only a very slight and local effect upon the oxygen content of the atmosphere, the effects in water are often pronounced.   In the upper layers both of fresh water and of the sea it is the rule, at least in summer, for assimilation to predominate and cause an increase in oxygen content above that which would be in equilibrium with the atmosphere.   The thickness of the layer in which assimilation can take place depends upon the transparency of the water, and may vary from a couple of meters or even less in freshwater ponds to a couple of hundred meters in clear ocean water. The very transparency of the water means a low content of organisms and a correspondingly low intensity of the processes of assimilation. Where the light is insufficient for assimilation, oxidative processes by bacteria and animals predominate and the oxygen content is reduced.

Speaking generally it can be said that in the sea the supply of oxygen from the atmosphere and by assimilation and its distribution by convection are sufficient to ensure practically everywhere an oxygen concentration which is ample for animal life. Exceptions are the depths of certain basins like the Black Sea where circulation is practically absent. In the Pacific there exists over a large area outside the west coast of North America an intermediate body of water at depths from 300 to 1000 m in which the oxygen concentration is below 1 ml/l and in some places, as first discovered by the Dana expedition in 1922 in the Gulf of Panama, even practically 0 (Thompson, Thomas, and Barnes, 1934). A study of the fauna inhabiting these regions might show interesting adaptations.

In rivers a fairly high concentration of oxygen is also the rule, although slow-flowing rivers in the tropics carrying an abundance of organic material may have very low concentrations. In lakes the oxygen in the stagnant water below the thermocline is often used up during summer, and in smaller ponds conditions are very variable, and low concentrations of oxygen quite common. This is especially true of tropical marshes where the high temperature favours a rapid decay of organic material (Carter, 1935) which not only uses up oxygen, but also causes CO_2 to accumulate at the exceptionally high tensions of 16–32 mm.

Into the bottom deposits both in the sea and in fresh waters oxygen can only penetrate by diffusion from the water just above, as convection is practically absent. These deposits always contain organic material, and often the quantity of such material is quite high. Oxygen is used up, mainly by bacterial processes, and the result is that generally only the surface down to a depth of a few mm and sometimes even

less contain any free oxygen. Further down anaërobic bacteria reduce oxides and often change the colour of the deposit
from a light grey to black. The production of hydrosulphide
and methane in these layers is quite common, and in many
ponds bubbles of methane and carbon dioxide rise regularly
from the bottom and may reduce the oxygen content and
increase the CO_2 content of the water.

When oxygen is used up in the bottom at a fairly rapid rate
the water just above the bottom loses oxygen and, as pointed
out by Alsterberg (1922), a "microstratification" develops, in
which there is a steep gradient in oxygen content over a distance of a few cm. Certain animals like the *Tubificidæ* studied
by Alsterberg and the larvæ of some of the *Chironomidæ* (K.
Berg, 1938) react to this condition by building mud tubes up
to 1 cm in height. These are ventilated by undulating movements, and where the animals are sufficiently numerous
(3,000 per sq. m.) they may succeed in drawing down sufficient oxygen (at a very low concentration) to keep the walls
of the tubes and the surface of the mud in the oxidized state.

In the following chapters many instances will be given of
the adaptation of the respiratory systems of animals to the
accessibility of oxygen in their natural habitat.

Carbon dioxide in natural waters. While the quantity and
pressure of CO_2 in the air is everywhere quite low, we find in
many waters a fairly large quantity at a low tension and in a
few cases even a tension which is too high to be negligible
from the point of view of respiratory adaptation.

The CO_2 of natural waters is only to a slight extent derived
from the atmosphere, but mainly from carbonates in solution.
It is not necessary for our purposes here to go into the complicated reactions between carbonates and free CO_2, but it is
necessary to emphasize that at neutral reaction an equilibrium will be established by which only a fraction of the
total will be present as free CO_2 which can pass the surface
and come into equilibrium with an atmosphere. When CO_2
is added (e.g., by a respiring animal) most of this enters into

combination and only a fraction remains free.   The quantity of free CO_2 can be defined and determined by its "tension" or pressure in an atmosphere which is in equilibrium with the water.   When a small amount of air (say 20 ml) is shaken with a large amount of water (say 500 ml) equilibrium will be established in a few minutes and the concentration of CO_2 in the air (determined by gas analysis) will give the CO_2 tension of the water (Krogh, 1904).   An increase in the amount of alkali, even in the form of carbonate, will lower the tension, while addition of acid will raise it.   In solutions which are more acid than corresponding to a p_H of 5, the CO_2 will be free and the tension may become very high.

In ocean water the CO_2 tension never varies much from the 0.23 mm which represents the equilibrium with the atmosphere.

It is important to note that even in carbonate-free water the CO_2 tension cannot as a rule become very high owing to the high solubility of the gas.   Supposing all the oxygen in distilled water saturated with atmospheric air at room temperature to be converted by respiration into CO_2, the CO_2 tension would only rise to about 5 mm.   By bacterial processes, e.g., the anaërobic fermentation of cellulose, so much CO_2 may become evolved that higher tensions are reached.

III

THE FORCES ACTING IN THE TRANSPORT
OF OXYGEN (AND CO$_2$)
THROUGH LIVING TISSUES

WHEN in a living cell oxygen is used up by metabolic processes its concentration is lowered and oxygen molecules will tend to diffuse towards the place. Similarly the CO$_2$ produced by the processes will tend to diffuse away. When blood possessing a higher oxygen tension and a lower CO$_2$ tension is carried past the cell all the time, the conditions for a regular exchange are established.

To the respiratory organs this blood arrives with an oxygen deficit and a surplus of CO$_2$, and conditions for a diffusion exchange with the outside medium are normally present also in this case.

A complete solution of the problem is not obtained, however, by these simple qualitative considerations. It remains to be made out whether the transport mechanisms are quantitatively sufficient and whether other mechanisms can be shown to exist. Certain physiologists (Chr. Bohr, J. S. Haldane) thought they could demonstrate an active secretion of oxygen from the air in the lungs into the blood, active according to Haldane (1922, pp. 208–257) during muscular work and after acclimatization to low oxygen pressures. Their evidence was inconclusive, however, and the only place where oxygen secretion has been shown to exist is in the gas gland of the swimming bladder of many fishes where it is bound up with very peculiar anatomical structures.[1] It is a strong, but not a conclusive, argument for diffusion and against active secretion that in the lungs of a small number of animals, including man, and in the tracheal gills of dragon fly larvæ

[1] It is probably present also in the gas bladder of several invertebrates and perhaps in the protozoon *Arcella* (Haldane, 1922, p. 216).

17

(Koch, 1936) oxygen has been observed to move *from* the blood (or tracheæ) towards the medium when the oxygen pressure in the medium is made lower than that in the blood (or tracheæ). This argument would not have much force if the epithelium was irreversibly damaged in the process, but in the cases examined it could function normally afterwards, and Koch even showed that the rate of diffusion in both directions through the dragon fly gills was the same.

A study of the quantitative aspect of the exchange by diffusion requires determinations of diffusion rates, distances through which diffusion has to take place, and quantities actually transported.

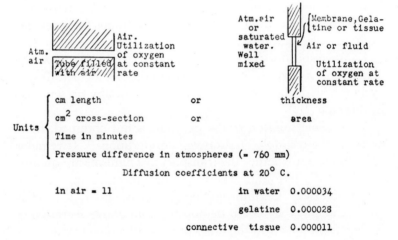

Fig. 2. Diagram illustrating a steady state diffusion of oxygen through an air space and through a membrane.

Determinations of diffusion rates can be made with least difficulty if a steady state can be established. Suppose that in Fig. 2 (left) we have a tube opening at one end to the atmosphere and at the other to a small space in which O_2 is used up at a known constant rate. In this space a certain O_2 deficit will be established and maintained, and when this is determined the rate of diffusion can be calculated. This rate is proportional to the area of cross-section and inversely

proportional to the length of the tube. The diffusion coefficient for O_2 in air is the amount (expressed in ml) diffusing
per minute through 1 cm^2 area and 1 cm length at a pressure
difference of 1 atm (= 760 mm Hg pressure). Corresponding determinations can be made on membranes as illustrated
in Fig. 2 (right) and a few results are here reproduced
(Krogh, 1919).

TABLE 6

DIFFUSION COEFFICIENTS AT 20°

in air	11	water	0.000034
		gelatine	0.000028
		muscle	0.000014
		connective tissue	0.000011
		chitin	0.000013

The rate of diffusion in connective tissue is just one millionth
of the rate in air, and generally the rates in watery fluids or
animal membranes are 300,000 to several million times slower
than in air.

It has been calculated for the oxygen supply to muscles
(Krogh, 1919) that thanks to the presence of an enormous
number of blood capillaries evenly distributed along the
muscle fibres the supply of oxygen by diffusion will be ample
even during the heaviest work—provided the blood is normally supplied with oxygen in the lungs.

No actual determinations of diffusion rates for oxygen from
the alveolar air into the blood are available, and both the
membrane thickness and its area are largely unknown.

The actual rate at which carbon monoxide is taken up in the
lungs of man, when supplied for a short time in low concentration (so as to be harmless), has been measured (Marie
Krogh, 1915, Bøje, 1933), and making certain probable
assumptions it can be calculated that diffusion will also provide the actual absorptions of oxygen observed during heavy
work and at high altitudes.

On the basis of these few experimental results we make tentatively the sweeping generalization that diffusion and convection are the only processes responsible for the oxygen transport into respiratory organs and within organisms.

The diffusion rate for CO_2 in water and tissues is about 25 times higher than for O_2, and it should be safe therefore to assume that diffusion is also responsible for the transport of this gas in solution. This assumption is strongly supported by the facts that CO_2 moves regularly in the direction of the tension gradient and that the tension in the arterial blood is always practically identical with that of the alveolar air.

IV

RESPIRATION IN WATER

ALTHOUGH the respiratory conditions in air are the more favourable, there can be no doubt that life in water is the more primitive type and we find there the simplest respiratory arrangements.

Respiration without respiratory organs and without circulation. In small organisms oxygen can diffuse in through the surface and reach every point within the body. Assuming a homogeneous spherical body in which oxygen is used up at a constant rate, the same throughout, and assuming further that the oxygen tension at the centre is maintained at 0, E. N. Harvey (1928) gives the following equation

$$C_0 = \frac{A\,r^2}{6\,D}$$

in which C_0 is the concentration at the surface, expressed in atmospheres, A is the respiratory exchange in ml/g/min, r the radius of the sphere in cm, and D the diffusion coefficient atm./cm/cm². With constant metabolism the necessary O_2 tension difference is seen to be proportional to the square of the radius.

Taking as an example a spherical organism with 1 cm radius having a metabolism of 100 ml/kg/hour or 1/600 ml/g/min and a diffusion rate the same as connective tissue (0.000011) we have the necessary oxygen pressure outside

$$C_0 = \frac{1}{600 \cdot 6 \cdot 0.000011} = 25 \text{ atm}$$

showing that an organism of this size cannot have the metabolism postulated if depending upon diffusion alone. Retaining the same metabolism per unit weight, the tension necessary for an organism with 1 mm radius would be 0.25 atm. or almost sufficient in water saturated with air, but when it is remembered that the metabolism is generally proportional not to the weight, but approximately to $W^{2/3}$ or to the surface, we find that even for this sphere the oxygen supply would be insufficient and, generally, that the necessary tension difference must be proportional to the radius of the sphere. The general conclusion is that when metabolism is fairly high, diffusion alone can provide sufficient oxygen only to organisms of 1 mm diameter or less, while larger forms depending upon diffusion must have a low metabolism. In many cases the assumption of homogeneity does not hold, and the diffusion coefficient for the surface layer may be definitely lower than we have assumed. Calculations have been made further on the assumption that diffusion takes place only inside the organism while the oxygen outside is replaced by convection. For many small organisms (eggs) which are immobile and have a specific gravity close to that of the surrounding water this assumption is not justified.

It is to be remembered on the other hand that the surface of a sphere is the smallest possible, corresponding to a given volume, so that conditions improve with any deviation from the spherical form and are a great deal better in threadlike animals. For complicated and branched forms calculations cannot be made, but it can be stated generally that from the point of view of oxygen supply each branch is independent of the rest.

This type of respiration is realized in a large number of small animals, viz., *Protozoa*, *Planaria*, *Rotatoria*, copepods, many mites, eggs and young embryos in all groups and young larvæ of many groups, e.g., within the *Crustacea*.

Some fairly large forms (*Spongia*, *Cœlenterata*, *Cirripedia*) also seem to depend exclusively upon diffusion.

The structure of the *Spongia* provides a very large surface practically proportional to the mass of tissue along which a continuous flow of water is maintained by cilia. In this case the size will have no influence upon the efficiency of diffusion.

The large *Cœlenterata* with less than 1% organic dry sub-stance have an extremely low metabolism, and water circu-lates slowly by ciliary movements through the gastro-vascular canals. The oxygen tension in this water is only slightly lower than in the surrounding sea (Backman, 1915). Henze (1910) found for *Pelagia*, the body of which is approximately a half sphere with about 6 cm diameter, that an increase above normal of the oxygen concentration of the water did not increase the metabolism, an observation which confirms the existence of a positive oxygen tension everywhere in the tissue. There is reason to believe that even in much larger *Cœlenterata* (*Cyanea* may reach a diameter of 2 m) diffusion will be sufficient.

In a number of *Actinia*, Henze's experiments show a definite dependence of the metabolism on the oxygen tension avail-able; the consumption, for instance, in *Actinia equina* (3 speci-mens in 500 ml water) rising from about 0.5 ml O_2/hour at a tension of 55 mm to 1.4 at a tension of 220 mm. This points to the permanent absence of oxygen in certain parts of the tissue. When the O_2 content sinks below 2 ml/liter, Pieron (1908) has observed *A. equina* to move to the surface of the water and expose more or less of its body to the air. When access to the surface is prevented the animals will secrete some mucus, close up completely, and enter upon a period of latent life.

The case of the *Cirripedia* will be mentioned below (p. 32).

Respiration combined with circulation. Assuming a spherical organism possessing a cuticle through which oxygen must diffuse while the transport inside the cuticle takes place by effective convection, we can calculate the tension difference necessary for the diffusion of the oxygen used in metabolism and we have

$$C_0 = \frac{A\,r\,T}{3\,D}$$

in which C_0, A, r are defined as above, while T is the thickness of the cuticle and D the diffusion coefficient for O_2 in the substance of the cuticle. Assuming as above $A = 100$ ml/ kg/hour $= 1/600$ ml/g/m, $r = 1$ cm, $T = 0.005$ cm, and $D = 0.000011$, we find $C_0 = 1/4$ atm. This would just about allow the necessary quantity of O_2 to diffuse in from saturated water, provided the tension just inside the cuticle remained at 0, leaving nothing for the transport by convection.

To account for the convection transport we must assume that "blood" arrives at the surface containing a small amount of oxygen at a tension which may approach 0. During its passage along the surface it takes up the oxygen passing in. The tension rises in consequence and may—when the conditions for diffusion are optimal—approach that on the outside. The mean tension difference must always be definitely lower than the outside tension. It can be found by a complicated integration when the tensions of the blood arriving at and leaving the surface are known.

From the formula it is seen that, assuming a constant metabolism per unit weight, the necessary tension difference is proportional to the radius of the sphere, which would mean a size limit to organisms respiring through the surface. When, however, metabolism is proportional to $W^{2/3}$ there should be no theoretical size limit, provided the thickness and permeability of the cuticle remains the same. In practice, however, these conditions do set limits to the possible size and determine the development of special respiratory surfaces.

FIG. 3.   Intraepithelial blood-vessels in the skin of the leech. A, in cross-section; B, from the surface.   (Hesse.)

Respiration through the undifferentiated surface is found in many *Chætopoda* (*Capitellidæ* according to Lindroth, 1939), *Hirudinea* (Fig. 3), *Gephyrea*, *Synapta*, *Pantopoda*.   In several forms there is no regular circulation, but the cœlomic fluid is kept in motion by cilia. Further in a number of transparent pelagic forms belonging to many different groups (e.g., larvæ of *Crustacea* and insects).

In a number of fish embryos and larvæ, circulation develops before the respiratory organs proper, and part of the surface functions provisionally as a respiratory organ and is provided with a capillary (Fig. 4) or lacunar (Fig. 5) system of blood vessels. In the young of *Acara* (a fish belonging to the *Chromidæ*) the tail is vascularized and functions as a respiratory organ.

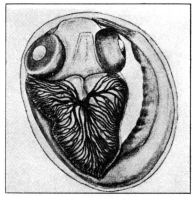

Fig. 4. Fish embryo (*Xiphophorus*) with blood-vessels on surface of yolk sac. Size probably a couple of mm. (Kryzanowski.)

In several cases it may be difficult to find out whether the whole of the surface is permeable to oxygen or whether special appendages function specifically as respiratory organs. H. M. Fox

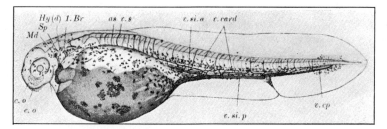

Fig. 5. Pike larva 6–7 mm long. Blood lacunae in yolk sac. (Kryzanowski.)

(1921) introduced the use of certain flagellates (*Bodo*) for this purpose, and certain luminous bacteria (*Bac. phosphorescens*) can also be used. Thorpe (1932) describes the culture of the bacilli which require a rather high salt concentration, and also of the flagellate *Polytoma* which he has found specially suitable. The flagellates show a preference for low oxygen tensions, but avoid water from which oxygen has been completely removed. The luminous bacteria require only a very low concentration of O_2 to emit light. The experiment by Thorpe illustrated in Fig. 6 shows that the first instar larvæ of the ichneumonid *Omorgus* absorb O_2 only through the body proper and especially through the fore part, but not into the "tail."

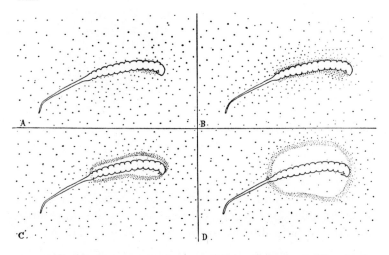

Fig. 6. First instar larva of *Omorgus* in *Polytoma* culture. *A*, after 6 min.; *B*, after 7 min.; *C*, after 10 min.; and *D*, after 15 min. (Thorpe.)

In a very large number of forms belonging to all major groups some oxygen is absorbed through the skin and CO_2 is eliminated, generally in even larger amount. When there is a tension difference, as is practically always the case, and when the integument is permeable, some gas exchange is unavoidable and all gradations are found between, this gas exchange being respectively essential or negligible in the economy of the animal. The accessory cutaneous respiration in certain animals will be discussed below (p. 54).

Specific respiratory organs show a specially enlarged surface in contact with the external medium through which more oxygen is absorbed (CO_2 eliminated) than corresponding to the metabolism of the organ itself.

The surface of an animal can be enlarged, either by being turned *in* to form cavities of increasing complexity, or by being turned *out* to form appendages. We shall designate all cavities serving respiratory purposes as lungs and all respiratory appendages as gills. As will be shown in some detail below, lungs are the typical organs for air breathing and gills for the respiration of dissolved oxygen. Nevertheless we find a few examples of lungs for water breathing and a larger number of gills for air breathing. Both lungs and gills often serve other purposes besides respiration, and it is sometimes difficult to decide whether cavities or appendages have any definite respiratory function.

Respiratory organs have been described in several minute worms possessing a well-developed circulatory system (e.g., *Dero*). Their function as such is extremely doubtful.

Generally a convection transport of oxygen by a circulating fluid is essential for the function of respiratory organs, but there are certain exceptions, and we have in the tracheal respiration, to be dealt with in a separate chapter, a system which is independent in principle of any circulation.

Water lungs are found in the *Holothuria* (Fig. 7). They are branched thin-walled tubes stretching from the anus throughout the length of the body. By contractions of the body wall they are at irregular intervals emptied (completely?) and

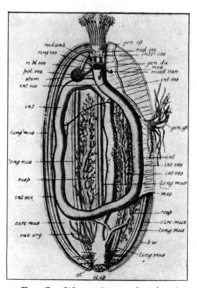

Fig. 7. Water lungs (*resp.*) of a *Holothurian*, opened along the middle of the dorsal surface. (Leuckart.)

again filled with sea water. There can be no doubt about their respiratory function, since oxygen is absorbed from their content, but they cannot be very effective. Bertolini (1935) believed on the basis of inaccurate analyses that oxygen was absorbed through their walls by a process of active secretion, but v. Buddenbrock (1938) has shown that it is unnecessary to assume anything but diffusion. When no mixing of the water inside the "lungs" can take place the absorption by diffusion must be a slow process. Although circulation of the body fluid is described by Kawamoto (1927) it seems to be poorly developed and it appears possible that the alternate filling and emptying of the respiratory tree may help to mix the contents of the body cavity.

In a number of *Annelida*, respiration through the walls of the gut, acting as a lung by taking up water, has been assumed, but the evidence is unsatisfactory.

Eisig (1881) studied *Hesione sicula*, a rather robust worm of a few cm length living in Posidonia (*Potamogetonaceæ*, nearly related to *Zostera*) meadows from the shore down to about 30 m along the coast of southern Italy. He found that the stomach contains bubbles of gas, especially in two diverticula which he calls swimming bladders. He assumes a regular uptake of sea water and a separation of gas for respiratory purposes from this water. He overlooked the fact that the intercellular spaces of the plants regularly contain gas which is also given off as bubbles, at least in the daytime. The gas is mainly oxygen from the assimilation process, and it is much more likely that the worms obtain their gas bubbles from this source. It is quite possible that the oxygen obtained in this way is of some respiratory significance, but there is no proof, and cutaneous respiration may very likely be sufficient for the animal's needs. Similar bladders, also containing gas, were found in *Syllis aurantiaca*.

Stephenson (1913) describes antiperistalsis and ciliary movements ascending from the anus in a large number of *Oligochæta* and *Polychæta*, and assumes these movements to be respiratory. Lindroth (1938) denies, however, that there is any effective water uptake per anum in the *Polychæta* with the possible exception of *Owenia*. In any case the volume of water "respired" seems to be so small that a primary respiratory function is unlikely. In the large worm *Aphrodite aculeata* Stephenson described a swallowing of water for respiratory purposes which is again expelled through the anus, but according to Lindroth (personal communication) this is a mistake and the gills on the parapodia are the only respiratory organs.

Alsterberg in 1922 described carefully the respiratory mechanisms of the small threadlike fresh-water worms *Tubificidæ*, building tubes in very soft organic mud which is practically O_2-free and absorbs O_2 at a rapid rate by the activity of micro-organisms. The behaviour of the worms depends upon the oxygen content of the water just above the mud. The gradient is usually very steep. Oxygen may be present just above the mud in which case the animals behave as shown in Fig. 8a. With increasing distance to water containing

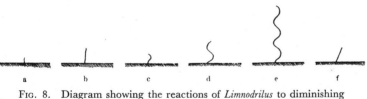

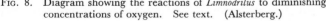

a   b   c   d   e   f

FIG. 8. Diagram showing the reactions of *Limnodrilus* to diminishing concentrations of oxygen. See text. (Alsterberg.)

dissolved oxygen, the animals stretch out their tails farther and farther and make rhythmic oscillatory movements by which water containing oxygen can be brought down from a vertical distance of a few cm. When this does not suffice and the O_2 concentration in the immediate vicinity of the animal (*Limnodrilus*) sinks below 0.08 ml/l (1.5 mm O_2 tension), reversible asphyxia is produced, and the worms become immobile (Fig. 7f). Certain forms (*Tubifex*) will migrate from the habitat before asphyxiation occurs.

Alsterberg observed antiperistaltic movements of the hind gut and believes that intestinal respiration plays a major part in the economy of the *Tubificidæ*.   As far as can be judged from his description, the amount of water entering the intestine must be quite small, and when the O_2 content is very low, as is the rule, the amount of O_2 to be obtained in this way is negligible and it appears much more likely that respiration is almost exclusively cutaneous.   It seems difficult to understand how the worms avoid losing much oxygen by diffusion into the mud from the fore part of the body, and it would be well worth studying these worms by means of flagellate indicators and perhaps the luminous bacteria, which will react to minimum concentrations of O_2, to find out whether oxygen is perhaps absorbed only through the tail while the fore part is impermeable to the gas.   A study of the affinity of *Tubifex* hæmoglobin for oxygen (cp. p. 104) would also probably yield interesting results.

In an echiuroid worm *Urechis caupo* living in burrows in tidal flats along the Pacific coast of America and studied by V. E. Hall (1931) and Redfield and Florkin (1931), ventilation of the hind gut acting as a water lung has been definitely established.   The integument is very thick and ill adapted to respiration.   The hind gut is a large thin-walled sack, stretching along the whole length of the body.   Water is taken into this sack by a series of small inhalations and again expelled by one large exhalation.   Antiperistaltic waves run over the hind gut all the time and mix both the water and the cœlomic fluid, which contains a large number of corpuscles carrying hæmoglobin.   Hall measured on a 60 g animal a total ventilation of the (artificial) burrow of 29 ml/minute when the animal was feeding.   When not feeding the worm would pump about 13 ml/m, of which one-half was taken into the hind gut where about 1/3 of the oxygen would be utilized.

Many of the fresh-water *Pulmonata* (*Limnæa, Planorbis*) can live at considerable depths, and their lungs are then filled with water.   It is possible that they ventilate the lungs with water, but much more likely that they obtain the oxygen through the general surface.   (Precht [1939] gives the references to numerous, but not conclusive, studies.)   Without mechanical ventilation water-filled lungs are useless for respiration, as diffusion will be much too slow to provide any significant amount of oxygen.

Two soft-shelled river turtles, *Amyda mutica* and *Aspidonotus spirifer*, both belonging to the family *Trionychidæ*, have been observed by Simon and Susanna Gage (1886) to ventilate their mouth and pharynx with water about 16 times per minute when submerged and to absorb oxygen through villus-like, richly vascularized processes covering the mucous membrane of the pharynx. Special experiments will be required to see whether any significant quantity of oxygen can be obtained by this mechanism.

On the whole it seems clear that respiration by ventilation of lung-like organs with water is resorted to more or less accidentally by a small number of animals only.

Branchial respiration. The normal way for aquatic animals to supplement the respiration through the general body surface is by appendages which are in the zoölogical literature usually called gills when no other major function can be assigned to them. We find all possible transitions between gills which provide only a small supplement to the exchange taking place through the general surface, and highly specialized structures, the sole function of which is the gas-exchange which they have taken over almost completely.

The more primitive gills are appendages on the outer surface of the animal, the more complex and efficient are enclosed in a gill cavity which has to be ventilated by a flow of water. Only in some of these latter can the function be studied by quantitative experimentation.

Certain appendages are called gills, although a respiratory function is doubtful or almost certainly absent. The "anal gills" of *Diptera* larvæ are normally salt-absorbing (Koch, 1938) and not respiratory, and it appears that the so-called "ventral gills" of *Chironomid* larvæ absorb oxygen at a slower rate than the rest of the body surface (Harnisch, 1937).

Among the *Cirripedia*, filamentary appendages attached to the cirri in 4 genera of *Lepadidæ* are described as gills, but their function as such is very doubtful, and the large majority of the species do well without (Darwin, I, p. 38, 1851). In the *Balanidæ* special "branchial" organs are attached on each side to the wall of the "sack," and ventilating movements are described by Darwin (II, p. 63, 1854). No circulatory organs have been detected, and it is relevant to point out that without circulation the "gills" cannot possibly provide oxygen for more than their own substance.

Small and very primitive gills are found in the *Asteridæ* while those in the *Echinoidæ* are generally more elaborate and specialized. The water outside and the cœlomic fluid inside these organs is kept in motion by cilia. In both groups a considerable proportion of the exchange no doubt takes place through the tube feet and other appendages.

In many *Polychæta* (*Nereis*) the parapodia are richly supplied with blood and function as gills, while in others (*Arenicola*) special appendages, with feathering branches growing out from the parapodia, have taken over most of the function. In some *Polychæta* (*Dasybranchus*, Eisig, 1887) the branchial tufts can be readily retracted into the body, and such movements are regularly utilized to renew the water along their surface. Such renewal takes place in many cases by ciliary movements (nudibranchs), in others by the locomotor activity of the organism as a whole (*Phyllopoda*), while in some animals muscles cause irregular or rhythmic movements of the branchial tufts (*Amphibia*, *Ephemerid* larvæ), and in others again there are special appendages which by their movements produce a flow of water along the gills (many *Crustacea*).

In a fairly large number of insect larvæ (*Ephemeridæ*, *Odonata*, *Trichoptera*, *Coleoptera*) we find free tracheal gills. So far as the exchange of gases is concerned these function just like blood gills, but the transport mechanism between the gill and the rest of the body is not a circulating fluid, but diffusion in air tubes which can be effective because the rate of diffusion in air is about 1 million times more rapid than in the tissue (p. 19).

In several larval forms of fishes (*Elasmobranchii*, *Polypteridæ*, *Dipnoi*) and *Amphibia* we find external gills in the form of threads or fine feathers. Babák (1907) showed that the gills which grow out in young tadpoles of *Rana temporaria* become large when the water is poor in oxygen and rudimentary when the water is saturated with the gas. Drastich (1925) made similar experiments on the larvæ of *Salamandra*. At a tension of 80 mm the gills were much larger and much more thin-walled than at a tension of 750 mm (Fig. 9), but in spite of the adaptation, metabolism was reduced and the growth slower.

Fig. 9. Gills of *Salamandra* larvæ. *A*, at 80 mm O_2 tension and *B*, in pure oxygen. (Drastich.)

The most remarkable development of functional gills is that taking place in the male *Lepidosiren* during the period when the fish attends to the eggs and young in the burrow constructed for the purpose (Agar, 1908). Shortly before the mating, filaments grow out on the pelvic fins which finally attain the development shown in Fig. 10. Agar definitely states that during this period the male remains in the nest and does not come to the surface to breathe air, as it does regularly at all other times. Cunningham (1929) and Cunningham and Reid (1932) put forward the hypothesis that the male provides oxygen for the eggs and young from his own blood through these pelvic fin gills, because they assumed that the water in the tropical swamps where *Lepidosiren* breeds is practically O_2-free. This assumption is no doubt correct regarding a large part of the season, but certainly not just after the rains. The *Lepidosiren* larvæ themselves respire from the water by means of external gills which begin to degenerate 45 days after hatching (Carter and Beadle, 1930) and the larvæ, which have by now attained a length of 40 mm, rise to the surface to breathe. At about this time also the pelvic gills of the old male begin to atrophy (Agar).

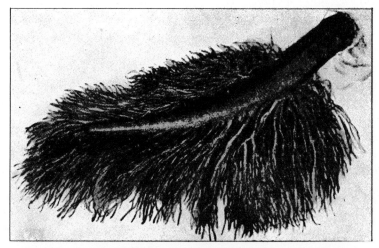

Fig. 10.   Functional gills on pectoral fin of male *Lepidosiren*.   (Agar.)

Gills in a cavity.   Gills protruding freely from the surface are evidently liable to damage and may be in the way during locomotion, and in highly organized forms we find the gills protected in a special cavity ventilated by a current of water. Owing to the low content of oxygen in water such ventilation must involve a rather large volume which must be brought in very close contact with the respiring surface, because the diffusion rate in water is so slow.   These mechanical problems are solved in different ways by different animals, and in some forms the efficiency of the mechanisms is very high indeed.

The primitive mode of ventilation adopted by *Ascidia* and most molluscs is by the beating of cilia.

In the bivalve molluscs and in the *Ascidia* we find gills with a very large surface, bearing cilia, and a flow of water generally much beyond the respiratory requirements of the animal. This flow is kept up for feeding purposes, and the respiratory function is incidental.

It is possible in some cases to measure the ciliary flow of water, and in most cases samples can be drawn from the incoming and outflowing water, and the oxygen content of these samples compared. This affords a measure of the respiratory efficiency, which is the higher the more oxygen is extracted from the water by the gills. The percentage of O_2 removed is called the utilization.

Van Dam (1935, 1938) studied the utilization of oxygen in the clam, *Mya arenaria*. Normally the utilization is very low, varying between 3 and 10%, but just after low tide when the animal has contracted an "oxygen debt" it may rise to 35%. The absolute utilization in one animal was found to be independent of the oxygen content of the water, amounting to 0.27 ml per liter water whether this water contained 15 ml/l or only 2 ml/l. In *Anodonta* a utilization exceeding 90% could be provoked by leaving the animals dry for 5–48 hours. Hazelhoff (1935) has observed utilizations of 7% on an average in *Lamellibranchia* and 6% in *Ascidia*. In all these animals the flow of water along the gills varies but little (at a constant temperature), but may be suspended altogether for some time.

Several marine worms construct U-formed tubes in the bottom material in which they live, and pump water through these tubes both for feeding and for respiration. Although their gills are external they are well protected and ventilated by muscular activity.

Nereis virens lives in shallow water and often in the intertidal zone in U-shaped burrows, from which it comes out for food. The animal pumps water at intervals through the burrow, and it is a significant observation of A. Lindroth (1938), who has carefully studied the respiration in the natural burrows, that the presence of a trace of mussel juice in the water, or a small piece of mussel meat placed outside, causes the pumping to be greatly increased and may call the animal forth from its burrow. The ventilation therefore serves both the purpose of smelling food and the purpose of respiration. When not disturbed, *Nereis* ventilates the burrow at varying intervals depending upon the temperature and the oxygen content of the water. At low oxygen contents (2 ml/l) the ventilation may become continuous, but at very low (0.6 ml/l) it *may* stop almost completely. The utilization of the dissolved oxygen is variable, but may reach the high value of 70%.

Arenicola was studied by van Dam, who found that the animal would respire in a normal manner when enclosed in a U-shaped glass tube as shown in Fig. 11. It is characteristic

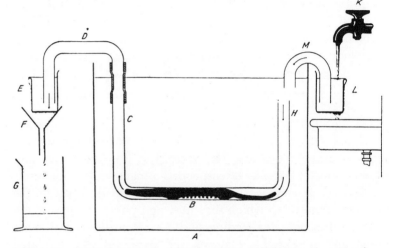

FIG. 11.   Determination of ventilation volume in *Arenicola*.   (van Dam.)

also for *Arenicola*, that breathing is intermittent. In one typical case there were pauses of about 20 minutes (at 20°C) and activity periods of about 10 minutes, during which about 90 ml water were passed through the tube. Thirty to 50% of the oxygen in this water was normally utilized by the animal, and it is a very interesting fact that the utilization percentage remained about the same, also when the water contained only 5% of the normal amount of oxygen or when the animal breathed normal water after a prolonged exposure to low oxygen.

In the decapod *Crustacea* the gill cavities below the carapace on both sides of the body are ventilated by the regular beating of pleopods. The frequency of this beating has been studied repeatedly (F. Peters, 1938; Fox and Johnson, 1934), and Lindroth (1938.1) succeeded in placing a crayfish so that the flow could be measured (Fig. 12).

The curve, Fig. 13, shows the effect of oxygen concentration upon the ventilation. At high oxygen concentrations in the water down to about atmospheric tension the effect is slight only, but at lower concentrations the ventilation rises abruptly, and the animal is characterized as dyspnœic when the exertion

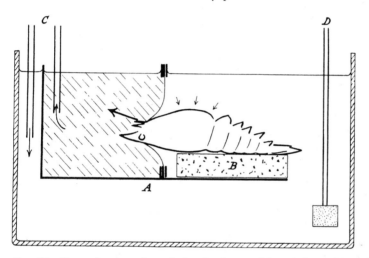

FIG. 12. Determination of ventilation in the crayfish. *A*, box with one rubber wall; *B*, fixation plate; *C*, connections to flow meter; *D*, aeration. (Lindroth.)

of breathing is a conspicuous item in the general behaviour. It is a very characteristic feature that the utilization of the oxygen is only slightly reduced in dyspnœa. In one case, for instance, the oxygen concentration was reduced in the passage through the gill chamber from 6.68 ml/l to 2.03 when the ventilation was 6 ml/minute, a utilization of 70%, while in another with a ventilation of 16.5 ml/min it was reduced from 2.10 to 0.86, a utilization of 59%. Somewhat lower utilizations, 49% on an average, were observed by Hazelhoff (1938) on a number of marine *Crustacea*.

In the *Cephalopoda* and especially in the cuttlefish the two feathery gills are located in the mantle cavity. Water is taken in along the edge of the mantle, but the cleft can be closed completely and the water driven out by a contraction of the highly muscular mantle through the funnel. This makes the respiratory movements serve also for locomotion and establishes a close correlation between the rate of ventilation and the muscular work involved in swimming. Winterstein (1925) measured ventilation and utilization in *Octopus*.

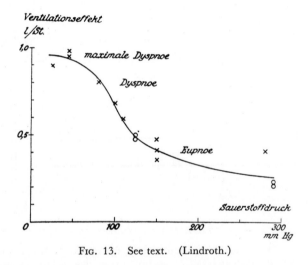

Fig. 13. See text. (Lindroth.)

He found that oxygen lack would cause an increased ventilation even to 10 times the normal. Increased carbon dioxide at tensions below 6 mm would also cause an increase, but at slightly higher tensions the respiration was inhibited. The utilization may reach 80%, but Hazelhoff (1938) observed an average of 63% in *Octopus vulgaris*.

The most highly specialized and effective branchial apparatus is that possessed by fishes. The gill filaments are arranged on gill arches (Fig. 14) between the mouth and the branchial cavity. As shown in Fig. 15, the gill filaments of neighbouring arches are connected in such a way that all the water passing between them cannot avoid a very intimate

contact with the filaments. Figure 16 gives a diagram of the
blood supply to the gills and shows the leaf-like secondary
lamellæ through which blood is flowing in a direction opposite
to that of the water flowing
between the leaves. This
counter-current principle is
of the greatest importance,
as emphasized by van Dam.
With blood and water flowing in the same direction

Fig. 14.   Diagram of gill arches in the
perch.   (van Dam.)

the maximum saturation of the blood would be determined by an equilibrium with the water leaving the gills.
On the counter-current principle the theoretical maximum
will be reached when blood leaving the lamellæ is in equilibrium with the water entering the gills, and even if this

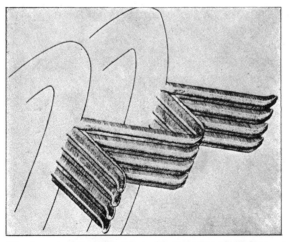

Fig. 15.   Upper part of two gill arches with two rows of gill filaments bearing
lamellae on each.   (van Dam.)

ideal is not practically attainable there is no doubt that the
oxygen tension in the blood leaving the gills is definitely higher
than that of the water leaving them.[1]   The efficiency of the

[1] The counter-current principle is realized also in the placental circulation
of some mammals (Barcroft and others, 1934).   From a functional point of
view the gas-exchange in the placenta is very similar to that in gills.

system is further enhanced by arrangements which, in spite of alternating inspiratory and expiratory movements, produce a continuous flow of water through the branchial system (van

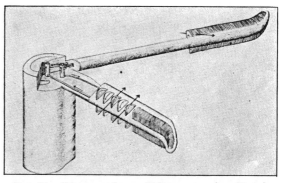

Fig. 16.   Diagram of two gill filaments.   (van Dam.)

Dam).   Inspiration takes place by a dilatation of the mouth and branchial cavity with closed opercula and opening of the mouth.   Part of the inspired water remains in the mouth, but part is passed through the gills to the branchial cavity. During expiration the mouth is closed, the opercula opened and the water contained in the mouth passed out through the gills.   Van Dam shows by an ingenious experiment that the pressure in the mouth of a trout is in both phases of the respiration higher than in the gill cavity.

The efficiency of the mechanism is well shown by the very high coefficient of utilization reached by fishes.   Van Dam, who made very reliable measurements of ventilation and utilization both on the eel (*Anguilla vulgaris*) and a trout (*Salmo shasta*), finds in both species a normal utilization close on 80%. Low oxygen concentrations and CO_2 tensions up to 7 or 10 mm increase the ventilation and may somewhat reduce the utilization.   The ventilation may be increased up to fivefold when the oxygen content of the water is below 4 ml/l.   This causes a decrease in utilization, but an increase in metabolism amounting in the eel to 40% and in the trout even to 70%. Van Dam gives very good reasons for the conclusion that this increase is due to the work of the respiration muscles. In air breathing forms the cost of increased ventilation is much smaller (p. 68).

There can be little doubt that fishes swimming rapidly do not make respiratory movements at all, but obtain the necessary ventilation of the gills simply by opening the mouth. Certain fishes, of which the mackerel (Baglioni, 1910; F. G. Hall, 1930) is the best-known example, are constant swimmers

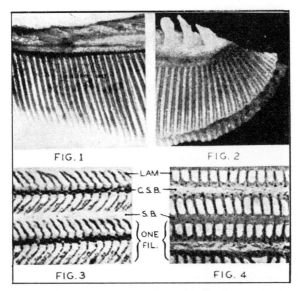

FIG. 1   FIG. 2

LAM
C.S.B.
S.B.
ONE FIL.

FIG. 3   FIG. 4

Fig. 17. *1*. Portion of gill arch in *Esox* with filaments attached. Magnification about 6/1. *2*. Similar view from *Amia*. *3*. Section through two gill filaments of *Esox*. Ca. 65/1. *4*. Similar section from *Amia* with central supporting bar *C.S.B.* Ca. 65/1. (Bevelander.)

and have lost the power of ordinary respiration. They cannot therefore be kept in aquaria, but only in ring-shaped or very large basins.

G. Bevelander (1931) describes a very peculiar gill structure observed in *Amia calva*, shown together with that of the pike in Fig. 17. The lamellæ of the filaments are joined together so that the whole is honeycombed, and large and very thin-walled capillary surfaces are exposed to the water. This *may*, as Bevelander thinks, be an adaptation to a low oxygen habitat, but the conclusion is by no means binding. At low O_2 concentrations a very high utilization is not called for so much as a large ventilation for which the honeycombed gills do not appear specially well fitted. It is conceivable that they may serve for respiration of air, although the capillary resistance of the very narrow passages must be rather high.

Branchial surfaces. Gill surfaces were measured in a few cases on *Crustacea* (Pütter, 1909) and fishes (Riess, 1881; Pütter). Pütter thought he could show that within the same species of fish the gill surface is proportional to the outer surface or, what amounts to the same thing, the square root of the gill surface divided by the cube root of the weight should be constant. This relation is rather probable *a priori*, but Pütter's measurements are not sufficient to prove that it is true. It seems certain, however, that gill surfaces per unit weight are larger in small specimens. When different animals are compared, some relation should be found to the maximal metabolism, but the material available is insufficient.

In the lower gill-breathing forms the circulation is not definitely adapted to the branchial respiration, but in most of the *Gastropoda*, the *Cephalopoda*, the higher *Crustacea*, and the fishes the adaptation is perfect, the venous blood being collected from all other tissues and passed through the gills before being returned to the general circulation. In the invertebrates the gills are located on the venous side of the heart, which is therefore the first organ to receive the oxygenated blood. In the fishes the heart is supplied with venous blood, and discharges directly to the gills. From the point of view of respiratory efficiency there is nothing to choose between the two systems.

Regulation of branchial respiration. The mechanisms for regulating respiration in aquatic animals have been the subject of a great deal of discussion. In many lower forms the regulation is very poor, or even absent when the movements serve other purposes along with respiration (bivalves, phyllopods, and others). In *Ligia oceanica* Fox and Johnson (1934) found the beating of pleopods, which produce the ventilating current for the gills proper, unaffected by O_2 except at very high and very low (< 2 ml/l) concentrations which both caused a slowing of the rhythm.

In *Gammarus locusta* they found that the pleopods need not move at concentrations above 5.6 ml/l. A fall in concentration caused a rapid beating which, however, slowed down again—even to 0—in 15 minutes with unaltered concentration.

In the higher *Crustacea*, *Cephalopoda*, and fishes there is no doubt whatever that oxygen lack stimulates respiration (Westerlund, 1906; Heerdt u. Krijgsman, 1939), while the effect of CO_2 is sometimes doubtful and never very pronounced (Olthoff, 1934; Helga Meyer, 1935). The normal CO_2 tension of natural waters is almost always very low, and CO_2 is certainly not a regular stimulant. It is contended (Winterstein, 1911, 1921; Olthoff, 1934) that oxygen lack may act by inducing an acid reaction in the "respiratory center," but this idea is purely hypothetical.

V

EMERGENCY RESPIRATION
THE TRANSITION TO AIR-BREATHING

In many localities, especially in the tropics, fresh-water animals are occasionally or regularly exposed to oxygen lack. For marine animals corresponding experiences are very rare, but the animals of the tidal zone have to adapt themselves to the fact that the water itself is withdrawn for periods of some hours or longer. In both emergencies air-breathing may be resorted to, but as a stimulus to evolution lack of oxygen is by far the more important. As organs for aërial respiration, gills are on the whole rather poor structures, and the chief reason is their softness, which causes them to collapse completely in air and present only a greatly reduced surface.

Certain animals living in the tidal zone have sufficiently rigid gills to utilize them more or less successfully for air-breathing. The opistobranch snail *Ancula*, which moves about above and below the water line, possesses quite rigid branched gills on its back. Several of the shore crabs (*Grapsus, Carcinus*, according to Raffy, 1935) have gills which are sufficiently rigid to allow them to obtain most of the oxygen needed from the air, and the large pagurid *Birgus latro* has adopted an almost completely terrestrial existence, even climbing trees. The gill cavities are incompletely divided by a septum, and the upper chamber, which always contains air, is provided with a·large number of rigid bush-like structures serving the aërial respiration (Semper, 1878). Several *Brachyura* (*Gecarcinus*) also live on land and breathe in a similar way.

In all these forms mechanisms are found for retaining some water to keep the delicate structures moist, and *Birgo* is reported to take to the water at intervals of about a day.

Even certain fishes belonging to the *Gobiidæ* and inhabiting tidal mangrove swamps in the tropics have become adapted

FIG. 18. *Periophthalmus schlosseri* on land. (Eggert.)

from a marine existence to a life mainly in moist air. The most specialized is *Periophthalmus*. Figure 18 shows the mouth and branchial cavity characteristically blown up with air.

The gill lamellæ have coalesced leaving only narrow slits, and the gills are unsuitable for water respiration (E. Schöttle, 1932). If the spaces can be air-filled they may assist the respiration in air.

When in fresh water the concentration of oxygen becomes reduced, many fishes and some other water-breathing animals will come to the surface, which by diffusion exchange with the atmosphere will present a microstratification with a comparatively high oxygen tension in the very surface. This reaction takes place in the dragon fly larvæ (*Aeschna*), according to Wallengren (1914), when the oxygen

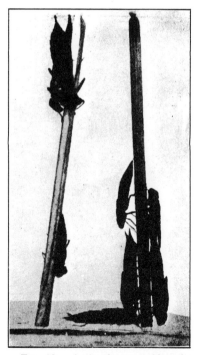

FIG. 19. *Aeschna* larvæ seeking the surface for emergency respiration. (Wallengren.)

content is reduced to 2.5 ml/l (55 mm tension), while a corresponding emergency respiration is not induced in the fish *Leuciscus erythrophthalmus* until the oxygen is as low as 0.6 ml/l (Winterstein, 1908).   Respiring from the surface, many animals will take in air which will increase the saturation of the water passing the gills, but is not enough to characterize them as air-breathers (Dighstra, 1933).[1]

True air-breathing can be accomplished in a large number of ways.

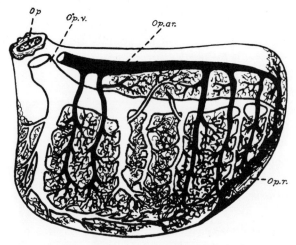

Fig. 20.   Vascular supply of inside of operculum in *Pseudapocryptes*.
10/1.   (Das.)

Carter and Beadle (1930–32) describe the case of *Hypopomus*, a small fish common in swamps in tropical South America. This fish can live in well-aërated water, even when denied access to the surface, but it will take in air when opportunity offers and pass it through the branchial cavities.   No special organ for respiration of air was found, and the gills appear to be used both for water and for air.   The secondary lamellæ seem to be unusually far apart, but they are not described as rigid.   Perhaps the air is used mainly to aërate the water passing over the gills.

[1] Also animals living in burrows in the tidal zone may aërate the water in their burrows during ebb, as observed by Lindroth (1938) on *Nereis*.

In an Indian inhabitant of swamps *Pseudapocryptes*, Das
(1934) found the walls of the buccal, pharyngeal and branchial
cavities, especially the operculum (Fig. 20) richly vascularized,
but the surfaces present no special enlargements.   When the

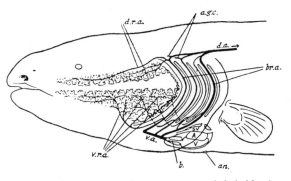

FIG. 21.   Diagram of accessory respiratory organs and their blood supply from
the branchial arteries in *Gymnotus*.   (Carter.)

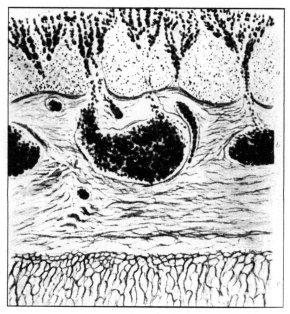

FIG. 22.   Section through part of a respiratory papilla with vascularized
epithelium, 60/1.   (Böker.)

fish is breathing air the operculum is kept closed and the whole cavity·alternately expanded and contracted.

In the South-American "electric eel," *Gymnotus* (= *Electrophorus*) the surfaces in the mouth and branchial cavities are enlarged by rigid excrescences supplied with a capillary net-work just below the surface (Figs. 21, 22), while the gills are reduced and unable to provide sufficient oxygen even in well-aërated water (Böker, 1933; Carter, 1935).

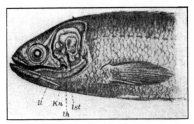

Fig. 23. Head of *Anabas scandens* showing respiratory "labyrinth" in special cavity. (Henninger.)

In several distinct groups of fresh-water fishes, of which *Anabas* (Figs. 23, 24) and *Clarias* (Figs. 25, 26) are good examples, special rigid outgrowths from one of the branchial arches, situated in a separate cavity with a valved opening, function as air-breathing organs, and these fish leave the water at night and often travel from one pond to another (Das, 1928).

In others (*Saccobranchus*) the branchial cavity is extended backwards as a long sac with richly vascularized walls serving the same purpose. In all these cases the organs are regularly ventilated by respiratory movements (Das, 1928).

A number of fishes again respire air by means of a portion of the intestinal canal.

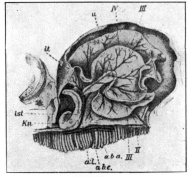

Fig. 24. Enlarged view of labyrinth showing larger blood vessels. 3/1. (Henninger.)

Some (*Ophiocephalus* and *Amphipnous*) develop pouches from the pharynx for the purpose, and in some species these are divided up by epithelial ridges into "alveoli" so as to present the same appearance as the lungs of

Fig. 25   Fig. 26

Fig. 25. Fourth branchial arch in *Clarias melanoderma* with respiratory "tree." (Böhme.)

Fig. 26. Respiratory tree slightly enlarged (Diameter about 2 cm in fish of 50 cm). (Böhme.)

frogs (Das, 1928). In *Plecostomus* and *Ancistrus* (tropical *Siluroidæ*) the stomach (Fig. 27) is a respiratory organ into which air is swallowed and again regurgitated (Carter and Beadle, 1930; Carter, 1935). In a number of other fishes, of which *Cobitis* (*Misgurnus*) is the best known example, more distal parts of the intestine are respiratory, and the air swallowed passes out through the anus.

Finally the gas bladder has been developed independently in quite a number of fishes either as an accessory or as the main respiratory organ, and this would appear to be the line along which the pulmonary respiration of the higher vertebrates has been evolved through forms related to the *Dipnoi*.

The criteria on which to base the assumption of the

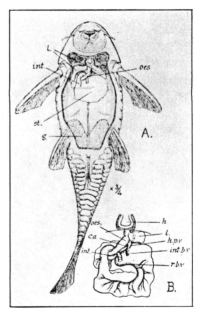

Fig. 27. Respiratory stomach of *Plecostomus plecostomus* 20 cm long. (Carter and Beadle.)

gas bladder or any other cavity as an air-breathing organ are first the regular or irregular renewal of the contained air. In a physoclyst fish the swim bladder can never be a respiratory organ, even if the contained oxygen is in times of distress used for metabolic. purposes. In physostome fishes mechanisms must be present for ventilating the bladder, and air must actually be passed in and out. In *Polypterus bichir* the gas bladder functions as an accessory respiratory organ only when the oxygen content of the water is low (Budgett, 1900).

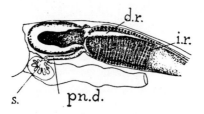

FIG. 28.   Air bladder of *Erythrinus unitæniatus*. *pn.d.* pneumatic duct, *i.r.* internal ridges enclosing alveolar spaces 1/2. (Carter and Beadle.)

The gas mixture expired must contain less O_2 and more CO_2 than the inspired atmospheric air. The difference in CO_2 is generally much less than the O_2 deficit, because CO_2 is given off also to the water through the gills and the skin.

Anatomically the walls of the cavity must show a respiratory epithelium with a dense network of capillaries close to the surface (Carter and Beadle, Fig. 29 *a, b, c*). In many cases, and probably always, when the gas bladder is the main respiratory organ, the internal surface is enlarged by epithelial ridges often forming distinct alveoli (Fig. 28).

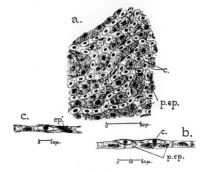

FIG. 29.   *c.* Capillaries in air bladder alveoli. *p.ep.* respiratory epithelium. (Carter and Beadle.)

The older anatomists placed a great deal of reliance on the character of the blood supply as a criterion, an arterial supply being taken to preclude a respiratory function. This has turned out to be a mistake, and the air-breathing organs in fishes are supplied with blood in the most diverse ways.

In a few cases (*Clarias, Saccobranchus, Hypopomus,* and *Symbranchus,* according to Carter and Beadle) the air-breathing organs are in parallel with the gills, receiving blood from the afferent branchial arteries and returning it to the dorsal aorta. This is from the point of view of respiratory efficiency the ideal arrangement, provided blood can be shunted from the gills to the air-breathing organs and vice versa.

In most other cases, including those in which the gas bladder is the air-breathing organ, the blood supply comes from the dorsal aorta and is returned through a vein to the heart. This means a great sacrifice in a respiratory efficiency which had probably been built up through a very long line of ancestors.

The blood coming to the "lung" is not venous, but is the same mixture which is supplied to all other organs, and the arterialized blood leaving it is mixed in the heart or before with the venous blood returning from the rest of the body. No organ is supplied with real arterial blood.

In the *Dipnoi* the first steps are taken to reëstablish by complicated vascular arrangements the respiratory efficiency of the circulation. There are separate pulmonary veins taking the arterialized blood through the incompletely divided sinus venosus and heart to the two first branchial arches, while a considerable portion of the purely venous blood passes through the third and fourth arches and goes to the lungs through a special pulmonary artery. This scheme is further elaborated in *Amphibia* and *Reptilia* and finally leads again to complete respiratory efficiency in the warm-blooded animals.

VI

RESPIRATION IN AIR

THE general properties of air are much more favourable to the acquisition of oxygen than those of water. In saturated water at 20° 1 ml oxygen is contained in about 200 g water, while 1 ml oxygen is present in 5 ml air, weighing only 7 mg, and at the same time the rate of diffusion of oxygen in air is about 300,000 times as rapid as in water. Diffusion will therefore be able to supply large amounts of oxygen over short distances, and the mechanical ventilation with air does not normally require the expenditure of much energy (see p. 68).

For the majority of organisms breathing air the restriction of loss of water by evaporation from the respiratory surfaces is a major problem, and accordingly the main respiratory organ is the lung, formed by folding the respiratory surfaces into a hollow organ in which the exchange of air is limited and can very often be regulated.

When in a lung a certain amount of oxygen diffuses into the organism it will normally be replaced by a similar volume of carbon dioxide diffusing out. The CO_2 pressure within the organism must be at any time *slightly* higher than corresponding to the concentration in the lung to allow diffusion to take place, and as an increase in CO_2 pressure can be tolerated only up to a certain point, this sets a limit to the utilization of oxygen. The general effect of CO_2 is somewhat similar to that of a narcotic, stimulating within certain narrow limits and above that depressing.

In a large number of air-breathing animals the CO_2 effect is utilized to build up a mechanism regulating the ventilation of the lungs (or tracheal system). This will be described in some detail below.

As in the water-breathing animals, we find a series of mechanisms of increasing complexity and effectivity running more or less parallel with the general level of organization.

Respiration by diffusion through the general undifferentiated surface and unassisted by circulation is the rule for eggs and embryos during the first stages. Many eggs (e.g., those of birds) are quite large, but the metabolism calculated for such eggs as a whole is extremely low. Most eggs are placed in surroundings where there is normally a high degree of moisture, but there are numerous exceptions among insects, and it is often difficult to see how such eggs avoid desiccation. It is possible for a membrane to be almost (or perhaps completely) impermeable to water and at the same time to allow the diffusion of some oxygen and CO_2, as found by Gray (1932) and by Krogh and Ussing (1937) for trout eggs, but the point should be studied on suitable eggs in air.

A few terrestrial arthropods of about 1 mm length or less (*Tardigrada, Pauropoda*) and also the parasitic *Linguatulidæ* which reach several cm in length manage, even as adults, without respiratory or circulatory organs.

In embryos at later stages the respiration through the general surface of the egg is aided by the circulation of the blood in the embryo and, as in aquatic eggs, there is often a network of vessels on the surface of the yolk sac.

Adult animals having circulation of blood just below the surface can attain a weight of several grams and a length of 30–40 cm (Earthworms, *Lumbricus*) without developing special respiratory organs when they live in a moist atmosphere, but most such animals are very small, like *Kœnenia* (*Pedipalpi*), many *Acarina*, and some *Apterygota*.

As in the aquatic animals, the body surface will generally take part in the respiratory exchange, even when specific organs exist, and in some animals this accessory function is, under certain conditions, of vital importance.

Cutaneous uptake of oxygen *must* take place when the O_2 tension of the blood and tissues just below the surface is lower than the atmospheric and the skin is permeable to oxygen.

These conditions are almost always fulfilled, although in some heavily chitinized insects the permeability may be extremely low.

There is reason to believe that in many pulmonate gastropods a considerable proportion of the oxygen is normally absorbed through the skin, because the lung can remain closed for long periods, while some of the aquatic (*Limnæa* and *Helicosoma*) can stay submerged for an indefinite time at low temperature (Cheatum, 1934).

The respiration through the general surface is of considerable importance also in the *Amphibia*, and the circulation is modified so as to distribute highly venous blood both to the lungs and to the skin.

A comparative study of the cutaneous and pulmonary respiration in the frog was made by Krogh (1904) and by Dolk and Postma (1927). The functional difference between the two organs comes out very clearly. By large variations in total exchange (70–170 ml/kg/hour) the oxygen intake through the skin, which is limited mainly by the conditions for diffusion, remains practically constant at about 50, while the variations are brought about by the ventilation of the lungs and the blood-flow through them. CO_2, which diffuses so much more rapidly, is eliminated at all metabolic levels mainly through the skin where the blood is exposed to an atmosphere practically CO_2 free. The elimination through the lungs is limited by the alveolar CO_2 tension and is therefore closely correlated with the ventilation.

In a small number of vertebrates (tortoise, pigeon, man) Krogh (1904.2) determined the cutaneous uptake of O_2. It is too small to be of any respiratory significance.

In blowfly larvæ having a very thin cuticle, Fraenkel and Herford (1938) find that in a normal atmosphere about 10% of the total oxygen is absorbed through the integument.

Air-breathing gills, formed by the internal branches of some of the abdominal feet and protected by the external, are found in some terrestrial isopods (*Ligia*, *Oniscus*) living in moist surroundings, but others belonging to the same group have developed functional lungs and have a greater power to withstand desiccation (*Porcellio*).

Lungs as physiologically defined are respiratory surfaces folded into the body. The gas exchange takes place through these surfaces between the "alveolar" air and the blood, and the gases are transported between the tissues and the lungs by the circulation of the blood. The distinction between lungs and tracheæ carrying air directly to the tissue cells is not quite sharp. In certain small insects and in several arachnoids the tracheal system is poorly developed and does not reach all parts of the body, so that some circulation is essential for respiration. Among the *Chilopoda* and *Arachnoidea* we have forms in which the tracheal system is definitely developed in the form of lungs.

Lungs are of two physiologically different types, viz., diffusion lungs and ventilation lungs. In the former, diffusion of oxygen and CO_2 between the outside air and the respiring surface is normally sufficient to supply the oxygen and remove the CO_2, while in the ventilation lungs a mechanical transport of air by movements which alter the volume of the lungs is essential.

Diffusion lungs. Diffusion is effective only over short distances and can serve for the gas transport to the respiring surfaces only in rather small animals. The largest are probably the African pulmonate snails *Achatina* and *Bulimus*, having a volume up to 500 ml.

Diffusion lungs are found in all the pulmonate gastropods, in the *Scorpionidæ*, *Pedipalpi* and *Araneidæ* among the *Arachnidæ*, in a chilopod, *Scutigera*, and in the "*tracheate*" isopods, especially the *Porcellionidæ* (Verhoeff, 1921).

It is a curious fact that in several quite unrelated forms diffusion lungs have taken the form of a system of numerous short and narrow tubes, generally called tracheæ, opening into a common vestibulum. This arrangement is found in the *Janellidæ*, a small group of naked tropical snails, reaching a maximal length of about 4 cm, in the isopod *Porcellio*, and in the chilopod *Scutigera*.   It provides a large respiring surface taking up only a small space in the animal.   A more detailed description can be given for *Scutigera*.

This animal has 7 dorsal spiracles each leading into a vestibulum from which about 600 short tracheæ arise (Haase, 1885, Fig. 30).   In an animal weighing about 0.3 g, Krogh

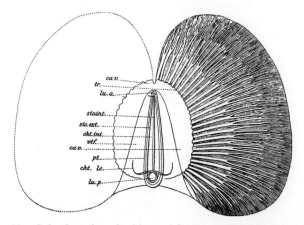

FIG. 30.   Spiracle and tracheal lung of *Scutigera*.   Ca. 60/1.   (Haase.)

(1920) measured the dimensions of these lungs and calculated the oxygen pressure difference necessary to supply the metabolic requirements.   This worked out at about 1 mm of mercury, showing that diffusion is ample, even if the spiracles are narrow enough to reduce considerably the diffusion rate. No respiratory movements appear possible.

Typical diffusion lungs are the "book lungs" of the lung-breathing arachnids (Fig. 31).   Plateau (1887) studied scorpions and several species of *Araneæ* and was unable to detect any respiratory movements.   The scorpions have 4 pairs of lungs (Fig. 32) situated in the third to sixth abdominal segments and receiving venous blood from the ventral sinus. Certain spiders (*Tetrapneumones*) have two pairs and others (*Dipneumones*) are described as having only one pair, but in addition a pair of "tracheæ." From a physiological point of view these tracheæ are analogous to the lungs. They do not supply the tissues directly, but serve mainly to aërate the blood in the ventral sinus. Lamy (1902) gives good figures from which the actual dimensions can be obtained for a considerable number of spider species. The "tracheæ" of *Heliophanes cupreus* which are unusually large and richly branched are shown in Fig. 33. Certain movements of the walls of the lungs have been described (Fraenkel, 1930) in several forms. It is very doubtful whether these bring about any ventilation, but certain that such ventilation, if it exists, is of no consequence compared with the diffusion which from the dimensions must be ample. Zoond (1931) confirmed this and demon-

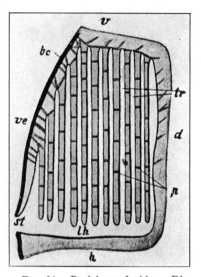

Fig. 31. Book lung of spider. Diagram. The length of the lung (*v-tr*) is about 1.5 mm in *Epeira diadema*. (MacLeod.)

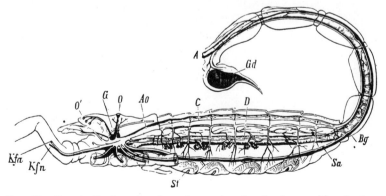

Fig. 32. Longitudinal section through scorpion showing lungs with spiracles, *St*. (Newport.)

strated the absence of cutaneous respiration.   Hazelhoff (1926)
showed on a number of spiders, and Fraenkel on a scorpion

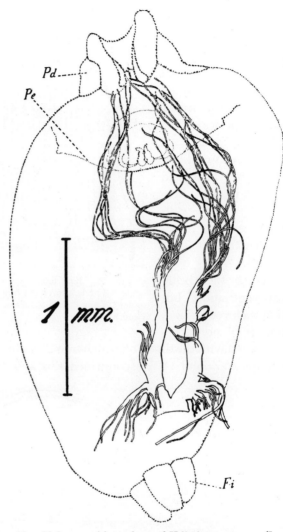

FIG. 33.   Abdomen with tracheae of *Heliophanes cupreus*.   (Lamy.)

(*Buthus*), that the spiracles remain almost closed when the
animal is at rest and the temperature not too high, thereby

reducing the rate of evaporation while allowing just the necessary diffusion of oxygen and CO_2. During muscular movements the spiracles are opened and remain open for a short time (1/4–2 m) after vigorous struggling. Hazelhoff showed that CO_2 is responsible for this opening, which amounts to about 1/10 of the maximal in 1% CO_2 and 1/2 in $2\frac{1}{2}\%$ CO_2. Special experiments showed (as in insects, p. 119) that local mechanisms at each spiracle sensitive to CO_2 are responsible and affect only that particular spiracle. Experiments with low oxygen tensions showed that down to 5% O_2 the spiracles would remain almost closed, and even so the diffusion is evidently sufficient. Lack of oxygen would give rise to an extra liberation of CO_2 which would cause the spiracles to open up, as it was observed at still lower oxygen concentrations.

In the air-breathing snails and slugs, both in the truly terrestrial and in the fresh-water forms, the mantle cavity is developed as a lung. This opens to the outside through a pneumostome which can be opened and closed. Part of the internal surface of the cavity is richly supplied with blood vessels, forming ridges which increase about 2–3 times the available respiratory surface (Dahr, 1924). The lung in the shell-bearing species is part of the mechanism for retraction of the animal into the shell. In *Helix pomatia* I have measured the volume of the lung when the animal was out to 5–7 ml, but when the snail is retracted it can be reduced to less than 1/2 ml. In the naked forms the volume is quite small (about 0.3 ml in an *Arion* weighing 10 g). The walls of the lung are muscular, apparently both in the shell-bearing and in the naked forms.

Dahr made measurements on *Arion* of about 10 g weight. He found the pneumostome to present generally a diameter between 4 and 6 mm, while the respiratory surface amounted to 6–7 cm^2. According to his calculations the pressure difference necessary to supply the lung surface with oxygen by diffusion from the outside amounts to about 2 mm Hg, and this shows that even in considerably larger forms and at low oxygen pressures the diffusion of O_2 and CO_2 in the air will be ample, and nothing can be gained by respiratory movements.

Nevertheless such movements have been described again and again (Maas, 1939). It is true that when the pneumostome is closed the pressure in the pulmonary cavity may be increased (Dahr, Ysseling, 1931), even up to 20–30 mm Hg in *Helix pomatia* (Maas), but these reactions have absolutely no respiratory significance. The closing of the pneumostome may itself serve to reduce evaporation (Wit, 1933).

Dahr found that at low oxygen pressures, from about 70 mm down to 15 mm, *Arion* and *Helix* show peculiar reactions which are taken to be "dyspnœic." These were confirmed for *Helix* by Ysseling, to whom Dahr's papers remained unknown. While the pneumostome usually remains open in moist air at normal O_2 pressure, it is closed at frequent intervals and for quite long aggregate times at low O_2 pressure. Dahr found, for instance, that at 15 mm O_2 *Arion* will close its lung 15–30 times in 10 minutes and for about 7 minutes in all. During the closed period the enclosed air is moved about by muscular contractions. In this particular case it appears that the oxygen lack causes a partial collapse of the lung, and the movement may serve to bring the air in contact with the whole of the respiratory surface. If the lung could be kept open and inflated the diffusion would provide definitely better conditions for oxygen uptake, the more so as the small amount of oxygen present must be materially reduced by the metabolism during the period of closure.

Dahr has shown further (1927) that at low O_2 pressure the metabolism is reduced by the insufficient supply of O_2. This is brought out very clearly in a series of comparative experiments on the same animal in progressive inanition. On the first day the O_2 absorption from atmospheric air was 110 ml/kg/hour, while in 5% O_2 (37 mm) it was only 33. On the second day the figures were 88 and 32, between the 11th and 14th 63 and 23, and after about 35 days 39 and 31 respectively, showing that at the low concentration the possible uptake of O_2 was the limiting factor.

No satisfactory explanation has been found for the "dyspnœic" movements of *Helix* in low oxygen.

The fresh-water *Pulmonata* were studied recently by Precht (1939). These animals move about on plants and stones under water and come up to the surface at intervals to breathe. Very often they contract the lung somewhat just before opening the pneumostome in the surface layer, but otherwise they do not make respiratory movements. Precht shows that two different stimuli serve to drive the snails to the surface to breathe. One is oxygen lack and the other is the amount of air present in the lung which serves also hydrostatic purposes. If a snail is exposed to an atmosphere of pure nitrogen it will remain as usual for a couple of minutes at the surface and then go down, but it will return very soon. An animal exposed to pure oxygen will remain the same time at the surface, but will return before the supply is exhausted when the volume of air enclosed in the lung becomes sufficiently reduced. A return towards the surface can also be induced, when the snails are breathing atmospheric air, by increasing the pressure to 2 atm and thereby reducing the pulmonary volume, and when the pressure was again reduced before the animals reached the surface they turned back towards deeper layers. CO_2 in low concentration has no influence, in high concentrations the narcotic effect is apparent. The relative insensitivity to CO_2 seems to be typical for diving animals, as we shall see later.

In *ventilation lungs* the exchange of air with the atmosphere takes place by volume changes of the lung. In inspiration the lung volume is increased, a certain amount of outside air flows in and is more or less completely mixed by convection and diffusion with the gases already there. In expiration a corresponding amount of the mixture is driven out.

Ventilation lungs have been developed only in the vertebrate phylum and are one of the essential conditions for the attainment of a large or even a medium size, combined with a high rate of metabolism, in terrestrial animals. By increasing complexity of structure they combine a very large surface area for the exchange of gases with very short diffusion distances within the air-space.

This is brought out by the somewhat diagrammatic Figs. 34–37. In Fig. 34 the whole lung comprises only one

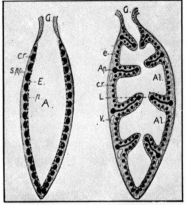

Fig. 34   Fig. 35

FIG. 34.   Diagram of unialveolar lung of *Proteus*, *c.r.* capillaries. (Renault.)

FIG. 35.   Diagram of *Siren* lung with simple septa. (Renault.)

"alveolus" with smooth walls containing a dense network of blood capillaries. In Figs. 35 and 36 there is an increasing surface development, but the whole is still one cavity, allowing mixing of the gases both by diffusion and by convection, and the entire surface is covered by the respiratory epithelium. In Fig. 37 we can distinguish both anatomically and functionally between the air passages, trachea and bronchi, in which practically no exchange takes place with the blood, and the alveolar spaces.   During inspiration air enters the alveoli from the passages and from the outside, and when it flows in rapidly it becomes mixed with the alveolar air.   As a continuous exchange takes place through the alveolar epithelium, diffusion of oxygen and CO_2 molecules must also be a continuous process within the air space.

Fig. 38 is a diagram of a single unit in the human lung comprising a final bronchus, atrium, air-sacs, and hemispherical alveoli.   The size of such a unit is about 2 mm, and it is evident that conditions for diffusion within it must be very good.

In the frog *Rana esculenta*, Krogh (1904) found that a lung containing 5 ml air had a surface of nearly 100 cm² or 20 cm² per cubic centimeter.   In man different estimates have been made, and a fairly probable figure is 90 m² for a volume of 3 1 or 300 cm² per cubic centimeter. In the lung of the frog the capillary area is about 2/3 of the total surface. In man it would appear to represent even a larger proportion.

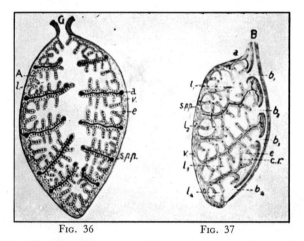

Fig. 36   Fig. 37

Fig. 36. Diagram of *Rana* lung* with complex septa. (Renault.)
    * In the species of *Rana* known to the writer the septa are more simple.
    Fig. 37. Diagram of *Testudo* lung with simple bronchial air passages. (Renault.)

In many reptiles (Wolf, 1933), and especially in snakes, considerable parts of the lungs have no respiratory epithelium and only a poor blood supply which is, moreover, often arterial. In the birds these "air-sacs" reach their highest development and will be discussed in a separate section. The functions of the air-sacs in reptiles are very imperfectly understood.

With the exception of the birds and a few mammals (elephants), in which the lungs adhere firmly to the ribs, each lung is freely suspended in a "pleural" cavity and connected with the rest of the body only through the hilus, where the main bronchus, the pulmonary artery and vein and the pulmonary nerves enter its substance. The lungs are highly elastic, and in most cases they will contract and drive out most or all of the air contained when the glottis is open and air is admitted to the pleura.   The elastic force resides mainly in a network of fibres, but the alveolar walls themselves and the capillary vessels, made up of epithelial cells only, are also highly distensible and elastic.   By inflation of the lungs the surface area therefore becomes increased and the thickness of the membranes separating the blood from the air correspondingly diminished.

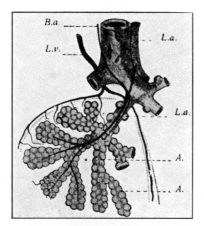

Fig. 38.   Diagram of alveolar unit in man opening from final bronchus. *L.a.* branch of pulmonary artery. *B.a.* bronchial artery. *L.v.* pulmonary vein. Ca. 25/1. (Stöhr.)

Experiments on the rate of diffusion of carbon monoxide into the lungs of man (Marie Krogh, 1912) make it probable that below a certain volume, corresponding to the normal expiratory position, the alveolar surface and epithelial thickness become constant by folding of the wall.   It is the rule that the finer bronchi have smooth muscle fibres in the wall, regulating the distribution of the air, and in many reptiles muscle fibres are present in the pulmonary tissue proper, and rhythmic contractions can take place the function of which is unknown.

The ventilation mechanism shows a characteristic evolution. In the air-breathing *Amphibia* the lungs are filled under pressure from the bucco-pharyngeal cavity by acts of swallowing and, when the glottis is kept open without such swallowing, the air flows out until the lungs are collapsed.   In some reptiles the swallowing mechanism persists and is sometimes used in emergency or (e.g., in *Chamæleo*) to inflate the lungs and air-sacs to a very large volume, but the normal mechanism in this group and in all the warm-blooded animals is inspiration by active suction.   This means that the lungs are placed in a closed pleural space which can be expanded by muscular movements and in which the pressure is lower than the atmospheric, at least in the inspiratory position. In mammals the thoracic cavity containing the heart and lungs is completely closed, and the pressure in it is "negative" in all positions.

The type and rate of ventilation varies greatly. In the *Amphibia* and many reptiles (all snakes excepted) oscillations ventilating only the bucco-pharyngeal cavity normally present a frequent rhythm, which is at intervals interrupted by a pulmonary expiration and inspiration. There is reason to believe (Lüdicke, 1936; Vos, 1936) that the bucco-pharyngeal ventilation causes no significant uptake of O_2 and only a slight elimination of CO_2, and Vos adduces some evidence (scarcely conclusive) to show that the main function is olfactory. He shows further that the complicated triphasic respiratory rhythms, assumed by older authors (Babak, 1912) for the pulmonary ventilation, were due to faulty technical procedures and that in all the reptiles studied a rapid expiration and inspiration is most often followed by an inspiratory pause of variable length. In the warm-blooded animals a regular alternation of inspiration and expiration is the rule.

The regulation of the mechanical respiration is a very complicated affair. Both the rate and the depth of respiratory movements are subject to a large number of reflex stimuli and inhibitions and vary accordingly, but given constant conditions of total metabolism the ventilation, which is the product of rate and depth, is far less variable than each of the two factors, because the depth decreases when the rate increases, and vice versa. The rightly famous experiments of Haldane and Priestley (1905) showed for man that the ventilation is governed mainly by the alveolar CO_2 pressure which remains constant at a constant rate of metabolism and increases slightly with large increases in metabolism. Since the arterial blood is practically in CO_2-tension equilibrium with the alveolar air, the results of Haldane and Priestley could be most easily explained by assuming an effect of the CO_2-tension in the arterial blood on the "respiratory center" in the medulla oblongata. In a long-standing controversy it was debated whether CO_2 acted as such or by virtue of its acid properties in solution. The balance of evidence is definitely in favour of the specific action of CO_2 (M. Nielsen, 1936). The sensitivity of the center is high (but, as we shall see later, subject to definite influences from other parts of the nervous system). Breathing of CO_2 in concentrations up to about 6% therefore greatly increases ventilation, raising the alveolar CO_2 comparatively slightly. At higher concentrations a narcotic and depressing influence makes itself felt. The CO_2 effect has been demonstrated for a number of air-breathing vertebrates belonging to all classes (Vos, 1936), but strictly quantitative work has been done mainly on man.

The constancy of alveolar CO_2 tension corresponding to a constant production of the gas means that alveolar ventilation must remain constant, while total ventilation may vary. This is important for the temperature regulating function of respiration. The expired air is saturated with moisture at a temperature slightly below that of the body, and a considerable amount of heat can be eliminated with water vapour by the ventilation. By increasing the frequency and lowering the depth of breathing total ventilation can be increased with a constant low alveolar ventilation, because the ventilation of the "dead space" of the air passages is proportional to the frequency only. This is a mechanism for heat dissipation utilized by many mammals and birds and often seen in dogs in hot weather or after exertions.

Respiration during muscular work in man. As emphasized on p. 7, the performance of the respiratory organs during maximum sustained activity is the real test of their efficiency. In man alone among animals the relation between muscular activity and respiration is quantitatively well known.

It is therefore appropriate to discuss conditions during work in man. When increasing amounts of work are performed by the same trained individual on an "ergometer," which measures accurately the amount of work, a linear relationship as shown in Fig. 39 is found between the rate of work and the metabolism as measured by the oxygen uptake. One set of results, marked ·, were obtained on an ordinary bicycle ergometer on which the subject must keep himself fixed by

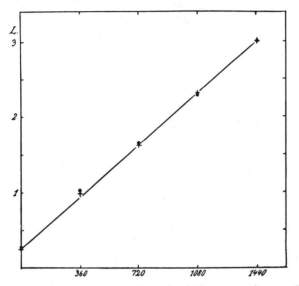

Fig. 39. Relation between oxygen absorption in liters per minute and rate of work in kgm per min. in a human subject. (M. Nielsen.)

gripping the handle bars, while the others were obtained with the subject working the ergometer in a reclining position in an easy chair. In spite of this difference the results are identical. The maximum O_2 uptake in a trained athlete is between 4 and 5 l/min. From determinations of the diffusion of carbon monoxide from the alveolar air into the blood of human subjects, Bøje (1936) calculates a maximum O_2 uptake of 4.5 l/min. Special experiments (M. Nielsen and O. Hansen, 1937) with breathing of oxygen-enriched air show, however, that the diffusion rate of oxygen into the blood is not the limiting factor for the O_2 absorption. There is reason to suspect that the results of diffusion determinations are systematically too low (Hartridge and Roughton, 1927).

The relation between ventilation and O_2 uptake is shown in Fig. 40. It is a straight line up to a ventilation of about 50 l/min; above that the ventilation increases more than the O_2 uptake with the result that the O_2 concentration in the alveoli rises. The maximum ventilation observed is about 120 l/min.

The increase in metabolism due to the work of ventilating the lungs was carefully studied by Liljestrand (1918) and later by M. Nielsen (1936), who extended the determinations to high rates of ventilation. Up to a ventilation of about 20 l/min the cost is about 1/2 ml O_2/l, or 1.3% of the resting metabolism, and not very different in different individuals. Larger ventilations are obtained as a rule by first increasing the depth up to about half maximal, which seems to be the most economical, and further by increasing the rate. At these larger ventilations the size

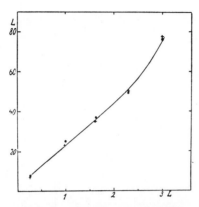

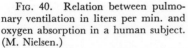

Fig. 40. Relation between pulmonary ventilation in liters per min. and oxygen absorption in a human subject. (M. Nielsen.)

of the lungs makes itself felt so that the cost is larger for smaller lungs, and the cost per liter rises rapidly with the ventilation, reaching not less than 5% of the total metabolism or a cost of 2 ml/l in a person doing 1,900 kgm/min with a ventilation of 116 l/min.

The regulation of the ventilation during work is more complicated than during rest but, as shown by Fig. 40, just as precise. That an increase in CO_2 tension is insufficient to bring about the maximum increase in ventilation is shown by the fact that by addition of CO_2 to the inspired air during rest the ventilation cannot be increased beyond about 60 l/min, and, as a matter of fact, the CO_2 percentage in the alveolar air during work is generally not increased at all. The chief mechanism appears to be an increase in sensitivity towards

CO_2 of the respiratory center which can easily be demonstrated by having a subject breathe, say, 3% CO_2 during rest and during work respectively (M. Nielsen, 1936).

Experiments on a few subjects (Krogh and Lindhard, 1913) showed that in these the very beginning of muscular work brought about a sudden increase in ventilation, but this is not universal. During the first minute or two of constant work there is some fluctuation in ventilation, but a steady state is reached, usually after 3–5 minutes, in which the ventilation remains remarkably constant corresponding to the rate of oxygen uptake.

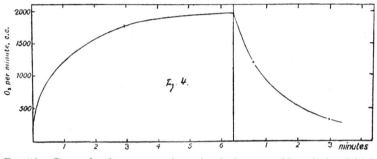

FIG. 41. Curve showing oxygen absorption in human subject during initial stages and just after work. (Krogh and Lindhard.)

During the initial stages of muscular work the uptake of O_2 is always lower than in the steady state and it is a characteristic fact (Krogh and Lindhard, 1920) that the "oxygen-debt" (A. V. Hill, 1924) thus incurred cannot be paid off while the work goes on at the same or at an increasing rate, but partly when the work is reduced (E. Hansen, 1934) and completely when it stops (Fig. 41). This involves a gradual return of respiration and circulation to the resting values over periods from several minutes to about one hour, depending on the severity and duration of the work. With bursts of maximal work over 1/2 minute or less the maximum O_2 uptake may occur after the work, and athletes can reach very high figures for the oxygen debt. Quite reliable figures of 9–11 liters O_2 are on record (E. Hansen, 1934), corresponding to the resting metabolism in not less than 40 minutes. Oxygen debts of 5–6 liters are easily reached. In several cases it was found that breathing of 50% oxygen which increases the supply to the working muscles would increase the amount of oxygen debt which could be built up (Hill, Long and Lupton, 1924). At a low oxygen pressure (high altitude) the maximum oxygen debt is definitely reduced (H. T. Edwards, 1936).

A comparatively small part of the oxygen debt is caused by depletion of oxygen stores in the blood and in the muscle hæmoglobin. All the rest was ascribed by Hill and his co-workers to lactic acid produced in the working muscles, but there is now a general agreement that a large fraction of the debt (perhaps about 1/2) is "alactacid": due to other and so far unknown split products.

During rest man cannot contract an oxygen debt, except in experiments in which the blood supply to some part of the body (e.g., the legs) is cut off. In experiments of this type a complete cessation of blood-flow to a limb can be tolerated for more than 20 minutes, and the muscles concerned will absorb afterwards an extra amount of oxygen amounting to at least 1 liter.

As we shall see presently, certain animals are able to build up an oxygen debt even during rest and utilize this power in prolonged diving.

The lungs and respiration of birds. The respiratory mechanisms of birds are definitely adapted to the function of flight, as evidenced by the fact that birds which do not

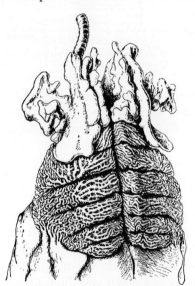

Fig. 42. Metal cast of lungs and air sacs of pigeon. Note recurrent bronchi from lower air-sacs. (Scharnke.)

fly (*Apteryx*, *Penguins*) show these adaptations in a greatly reduced form.

The lungs of birds are small and compact. They adhere firmly to the wall of the thorax, and a number of ribs are embedded in their substance (Fig. 42).

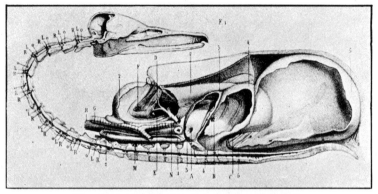

Fig. 43. Air-sacs of duck, inflated. (Sappey.)

Certain large bronchi pass directly through the lungs and open through wide "ostia" into spacious air-sacs (Figs. 43, 44, 45). It is convenient to distinguish between the anterior sacs comprising the two cervical, the single clavicular, and the two præthoracic, and the posterior comprising the paired post-thoracic and abdominal. The air-sacs are very thin-walled and have only a poor supply of arterial blood. No significant exchange of gases takes place through their walls (Soum, 1896). The two main bronchi arising from the trachea lose their cartilage shortly after entering the lungs and continue as "mesobronchi" towards the posterior ends of the lungs, opening there into the abdominal sacs. From the main- and mesobronchi a definite small number of primary bronchi lead to the other air-sacs and into the "parenchyma" of the lungs (Fig. 45). The walls of all these bronchi and their ramifications are pierced like a sieve by an enormous number of holes (about 1/2 mm wide) leading into "parabronchi." The walls of these again are a meshwork and open into air-capillaries of about 10 mikrons diameter. The parabronchi anastomose freely, as do also the air-capillaries from different parabronchi. The walls of the parabronchi are covered, like those of the larger bronchi, with a ciliated epithelium and contain numer-

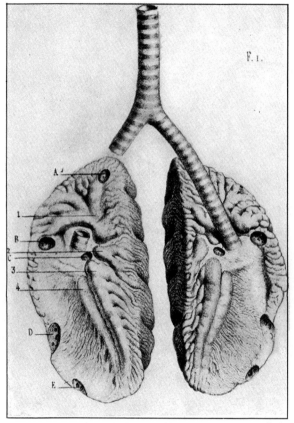

Fig. 44. Lungs of duck with ostia, opening into air-sacs. (Sappey.)

ous smooth muscle fibres. The walls of the alveoli appear to be made up of the endothelium of blood capillaries only, without any epithelium. It is a very significant fact, discovered by Schulze (1910) and by Juillet (1911), that "recurrent" or "saccobronchi" penetrate the lung from the posterior air-sacs (Fig. 45 s.b. and Fig. 42). These recurrent bronchi are slightly developed only from the anterior air-sacs. They are absent in penguins (Vos, 1937). Provided a sufficient number of microscopic anastomoses exist connecting the recurrent with the main bronchi through the parenchyma, the flow of air between the trachea and the sacs must pass to a corresponding

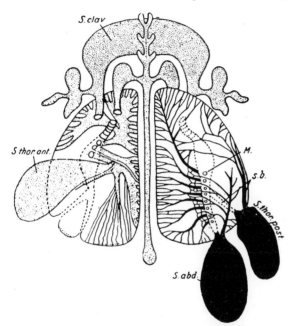

Fig. 45. Diagram of pigeon lungs with air-sacs. Left, ventral surface; right, dorsal surface with recurrent bronchi from abdominal and posterior thoracic air-sac. (Brandes.)

extent through the lung parenchyma. We have two connections in parallel, and the flow will be distributed in inverse ratio of their resistance.

The presence of valves forcing the air in definite directions through the pulmonary tissue has been postulated repeatedly (Brandes, 1924; Vos, 1934). They have never been observed anatomically, and the physiological experiments from which their existence has been deduced are inconclusive.

The volume of the lungs is quite small, but the air-sacs take up a much larger proportion of the total body volume than the lungs in mammals. Vos (1935) determined the volume of the air-sacs in the inspiratory position (less the cervicals) in a duck of 1.4 kg to 280 ml or 20% of the whole body (Table 7, p. 75).

By the respiratory movements in the normal standing position of a bird the whole thoracic and abdominal cavity is enlarged in inspiration and air is sucked into the lungs and air-sacs. This was first clearly recognized by Soum (1896) and a recent detailed study was made by Zimmer (1935). The movements are shown in figs. 46 and 47.

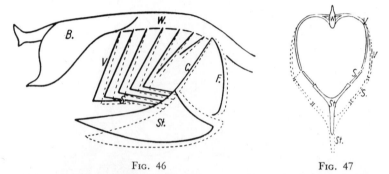

FIG. 46   FIG. 47

FIG. 46.   Lateral view of respiratory thorax movements in standing bird.
(Zimmer.)
FIG. 47.   Frontal view of respiratory movements.   Dotted line inspiration.
(Zimmer.)

A study of the distribution of the inspired air between the lungs and the separate air-sacs presents very formidable experimental difficulties, and from the literature anything but a clear and consistent picture can be obtained. Some information is available, however.

The lungs are expanded in inspiration mainly by the pull of the ribs, as observed by Scharnke (1938) and others, but just how much it has been impossible so far to find out. A pigeon on which all the air-sacs have been broadly opened gets very dyspnœic, but is not asphyxiated.

Experiment by Vos (1935), in which a duck was suddenly given pure oxygen to breathe and the O_2 percentage in the single air-sacs measured after a few respirations, go to show that the O_2 percentage rises rapidly in the posterior air-sacs and much more slowly in the anterior sacs. This means a larger ventilation in relation to capacity of the posterior sacs. Assuming, according to the measurements, a total volume per breath of 35 ml and a "dead space" (volume of air passages) of 4 ml, E. Zeuthen, in a paper to be published in the near future, has utilized Vos's results to calculate the ventilation of the single sacs. He finds 17 ml per breath for the abdominal sacs (12% of the volume), 8 for the postthoracic (14%), 1 only for the præthoracic (4%) and an insignificant volume (less than 1%) for the clavicular. This would leave $35 - (17 + 8 + 1) = 9$ ml for the volume entering the lungs during inspiration, but it must be admitted that this latter figure is very uncertain and the whole calculation should not be taken too seriously. Perhaps it is safe to say that at least 3/4 of the total inspiration ultimately goes to the air-sacs and at most 1/4 to the lungs. From the anatomy one would expect the dilatation of the lungs to be definitely smaller. Experiments have been planned to obtain more reliable figures by means of indifferent gases.

Several series of determinations have been made of the composition of the gas mixtures in the air-sacs of birds breathing normally. The most reliable are those made by Vos (1935) on the duck by introducing narrow cannulas into the sacs and drawing out small samples when the bird was absolutely quiet. These give for CO_2

TABLE 7

	CO_2 %			Average	Volumes
Interclavicular air	6.9	5.7	6.5	6.4	53 ml
Præthoracic "	5.9	4.4	5.1	5.1	24 "
Postthoracic "	3.3	2.3	2.7	2.8	57 "
Abdominal "	2.7	1.9	2.5	2.4	145 "
Total expired "	5.8	4.3	5.1	5.1	35 "

The well-ventilated posterior sacs should show a much lower CO_2 percentage if the air entered them only through the bronchi, and conversely the CO_2 percentage of the expired air should be much lower if the expired air was made up as indicated by Zeuthen's calculations of 75% air from the posterior sacs and 25% from the lungs. The inference appears unavoidable that both during inspiration and during expiration a rather large proportion of the air going to and from the sacs passes the parenchyma of the lungs through the parabronchial and alveolar anastomoses. As pointed out above, this is what one would expect from the anatomical structure, without having to assume the presence of any valves. Quantitatively the figures would indicate that in the resting duck during inspiration rather less than 1/2 of the air entering the sacs passes through the lung parenchyma, and during expiration rather more than 1/2 passes out along this route, but this is a very rough estimate. It goes without saying that the passage of air with a high oxygen percentage and low CO_2 through the lung tissue both during inspiration and during expiration must greatly facilitate the gas exchange.

It is important to remember that the parabronchi are well supplied with smooth muscle. The resistance to the passage of air *through* them can therefore probably be regulated so as to change the ratio of ventilation through the parenchyma to that going directly to the air-sacs. This is of importance for the heat-regulating function of the respiratory system. The birds are well protected against heat loss through the skin by the highly insulating plumage. They have no sweat glands and the evaporation from the skin must be of a low order and can be regulated, if at all, only to a slight extent. No measurements are available. Evaporation of water from the respiratory tract is therefore in birds, as in certain mammals (e.g., dogs), an important mechanism for heat dissipation and is regulated accordingly. Von Saalfeld (1936) found on a pigeon, which had at a normal body temperature (41.7°C) a respiration frequency of 45/min. with a depth of 4 ml, that by increasing the body temperature to 43.6° the frequency would increase to 500 with a depth of 1.25 ml only. This will enormously increase the evaporation of water and *may* leave the pulmonary ventilation proper unaltered. As we shall see, the regulation of heat loss becomes a very important consideration during flight.

The respiration during flight. When the study of the respiration in a resting bird presents serious difficulties this is doubly true when we have to deal with the respiration during flight. Until recently it was generally believed, mainly on the authority of Baer (1896), that during flight the thorax is absolutely fixed, while the ventilation is brought about by accessory sacs, mainly those diverticula of the clavicular sac which separate the wing muscles and may penetrate into them. These sacs are alternately compressed and dilated by the muscle contractions. This conception does not take into account the enormous increase in metabolism during active flight which necessitates, like other muscular work, a corresponding increase in pulmonary ventilation. Baer made the observation (repeatedly verified) that a rapid stream of air against the head of a bird inhibits the normal respiration (for a short time) and took this as a proof of his contention. Marey (1890) and Soum (1896) assumed a ventilation during flight by movements of the thorax caused directly by the beating of the wings. Soum showed that artificial wing movements on a dead bird brought about ventilation, and Marey definitely showed by graphic recording that in a pigeon the ventilation during flight is synchronous with the wing movements. Both Soum and Marey took it for granted that the down-stroke of the wings corresponds to an expiration, and it must be admitted that this is *a priori* much more probable than the opposite. Nevertheless the most recent study by Zimmer (1935) purports to show that the respiration during flight is in principle independent of the flight movements. It is, according to his graphic records, almost universally synchronized with these, but expiration corresponds to the up-stroke of the wings. I cannot accept Zimmer's records as quite conclusive and would prefer to leave the question open for the present.

Zeuthen attempted through aëronautic considerations to obtain some idea of the work performed by a bird during flight and to calculate the necessary metabolism and the amount of heat to be eliminated. The results, which must necessarily be very approximate, do indicate that during rapid flight the metabolism must be very greatly increased. A pigeon flying, say, at a rate of 70 km = 43.5 miles per hour would have to spend 14.8 Cal in overcoming the resistance. With a 25% utilization of the metabolic energy this should correspond to a metabolism of 2.3 (the resting value) + 59.2 Cal/hour or 26.8 times the resting value. It appears that a higher rate of ventilation is necessary to get rid of the extra heat generated than to obtain the necessary oxygen, and Zeuthen concludes that during flight the ventilation of the air-sacs is increased beyond that of the lungs. It will be interesting to have these theoretical deductions verified by actual experimentation. At present it is possible only to affirm that animal flight means a stress both upon metabolism and upon heat dissipation greater than any other form of muscular work.

It seems to be a general rule, holding also for bats (v. Saalfeld, 1938) and for many insects, that during flight, respiration is synchronized with the wing movements.

The respiratory and circulatory adaptations to diving. A number of the air-breathing vertebrates are able to dive, and some are able to stay under water for quite a long time. This ability raises interesting problems concerning their respiration about which we could until recently only make guesses. Thanks mainly to the work of Irving and Scholander we are now in a better position, and some points regarding the respiration of diving animals have been made tolerably clear.

Long-time divers are found in all the vertebrate classes. The *Amphibia* can remain very long under water, thanks to their cutaneous respiration, but in all the others the uptake of oxygen through the skin is insignificant.

Sea snakes are reported (Curran and Kauffeld according to Volsöe, 1939) to remain submerged for at least 8 hours and have been caught at depths up to 30 meters.

Crocodiles, turtles, and many tortoises, living in water, dive regularly and many of them are stated to stay for hours or even days under water (Vos, 1936). The concentration of oxygen in the lungs of the fresh-water tortoise *Emys orbicularis* under water falls to 2–3% in half an hour (Vos). The cutaneous uptake of oxygen which is normally of the order of 2% of the total, according to Lüdicke (1936), may increase to 8%, but it is evident that the metabolism must be either greatly reduced or become mainly anaërobic. No really quantitative work on the diving of reptiles has been made so far, although some of them should be very suitable for the purpose.

An excellent study of diving birds was made by Christian Bohr in 1895, but unfortunately the results were only published in Danish (1897) and have remained unnoticed until now. A rather full account of this paper will therefore not be out of place.

The experiments and determinations were made on guillemot (*Uria troile*) weighing about 700 g and puffin (*Mormon ratercula*—350 g). These will stand submersion only for short periods (up to 6 min. in the case of the guillemot), but they will go down, swimming vigorously, for a few minutes at a time with breathing spells at the surface of a few seconds only, and artificial submersions of the same type, each lasting 2 minutes, could be sustained at least 10 to 20 times. The blood volume and oxygen capacity of both birds were found to be high, namely respectively 12–13% of the body weight and about 25 ml O_2/100 ml. This means 30 ml O_2/kg animal as against 16 in non-diving mammals.

A number of varied and instructive respiration experiments were made, comprising periods in which the trachea was obstructed. I give as an example the determinations on a guillemot weighing 685 g., shown in Table 8.

The oxygen debt incurred during a period of obstruction is more than made good in the next 5 minutes, while an excess of CO_2 is blown off. In other experiments a small air sample (54 ml) was drawn every 2 minutes from the closed trachea and replaced with atmospheric air. This raised the CO_2 percent-

TABLE 8

	Normal	After 4 m. obstruct.	15–25 min. later	After 4 m. obstruct.	14–24 min. later	After 4 m. obstr.
Air expired/min.	324	448	162	592	189	320
% CO_2	4.83	8.64	5.25	8.17	4.17	7.43
% O_2	15.05	12.17	12.98	13.77	14.62	12.38
O_2 absorbed/min.	20.5	40	14.2	41.6	13.3	28.8
R.Q.	0.76	0.96	0.59	1.16	0.59	0.82
Time	5^{8-18}	5^{29-34}	5^{49-59}	6^{13-18}	6^{32-42}	6^{52-57}

age to 15%, while the oxygen dropped to 4%; conditions which the bird would tolerate and which show an unusual resistance against CO_2. In experiments involving the respiration of gas mixtures poor in oxygen it was shown that the birds would stand breathing 5–6% O_2 for a long time, while taking up much less O_2 than normally and eliminating either the normal quantity or an excess of CO_2. Given gas-mixtures with less than 1.5% O_2 the bird would be killed just as rapidly as non-divers and would lose oxygen from the blood to the air. Bohr ascribes this last result to a harmful action on the lung tissue, but damage to the central nervous system is a much more likely explanation.

Among mammals the greatest divers are the whales and among these again the sperm whale and the bottlenose seem to have the records for depth (about 900 meters) and endurance (1–2 hours) according to a valuable collection of data by Irving (1939). How is this possible?

The whales, especially the large ones, do not lend themselves willingly to experimentation, but very suggestive information has been obtained on more manageable animals like the seals, the beaver, and others.

The first point I would like to make is that in true diving animals of all classes contact of the respiratory openings with water stops breathing by reflex.

During the period of submergence CO_2 accumulates in the blood and would in terrestrial animals (at least in mammals) force the resistance against respiration, but it seems to be a general rule for divers to be much less sensitive to CO_2 as noted for the crocodile by Dill and Edwards (1931), but first clearly realized by Irving (1935, 1938).   This makes it possible for the diving animal to keep its breath.   There is a very interesting difference in behaviour, as pointed out by Irving and noted already by Bohr in the diving birds, which perhaps we should call psychic.   If a terrestrial mammal is forcibly submerged it will struggle violently and exhaust itself, while a diver will keep quiet so as to use the least amount of oxygen.   This is not, however, of essential significance, because it can be shown that while the divers carry a store of oxygen it is certainly inadequate to supply their normal needs during a diving period.

The store of oxygen carried by divers is not to any large extent carried in the lungs.   Seals frequently, perhaps normally, make an expiration before diving, and Scholander has recently shown that in whales who dive after an inspiration the lungs are small in relation to the size of the body.   It would seem that the air in the lungs may be used mainly to regulate buoyancy and, as we shall see later, there are good reasons why it would be fatal to deep divers to have a large volume of air in the lungs.

The oxygen is carried in a large blood volume and a high concentration of hæmoglobin in the blood, and in addition many divers, especially the seals and whales, have large stores of muscle hæmoglobin which are presumably oxygen-saturated when they make a dive.

Scholander made up the following balance sheet for a seal (*Cystophora*) of 29 kg.

TABLE 9

350 ml alveolar air with 16% O_2	50 ml O_2
4500 ml blood with 25 vol % O_2	1100 " "
6000 g muscle with 4.5 vol % O_2	270 " "
Other tissues and fluids	100 " "
Total	1520 ml O_2

With the oxygen consumption normally observed such a store might last for five minutes.

This supposes the seal to be absolutely quiet during the dive, but, as we know, the seal like the other divers does its swimming and catches its prey under water.   The seal must therefore contract a very considerable oxygen debt in addition to that represented by the depletion of the stores.   Scho-

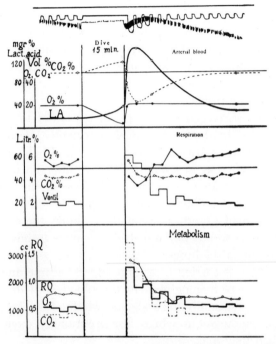

Fig. 48.   Influence of 15 min. dive on respiration, blood gases and lactic acid, expired air and metabolism in seal.   Explanation see text.   (Scholander.)

lander worked out methods for accurately measuring the respiratory exchange in seals and graphically recording the respiration.   The curves (Fig. 48) tell the story of one experiment in which the seal remained under water with suspended respiration for 15 minutes.   On top we have the actual record showing before the dive periodic breathing of the so-called "Cheyne-Stokes" type.   The diving begins with an expiration and when the seal comes out there is a deep inspiration followed by a period of continuous and very deep breathing, gradually lapsing in about 15 minutes into the normal resting type.   The lowest curves marked Metabolism give the oxygen absorption and corresponding CO_2 liberation in 3-minute periods.   Before the dive the gas exchange is fairly constant, during the dive it is suspended, and just after there is a large increase lasting for 7 periods (21 minutes) and covering in this case 86% of the debt incurred during the dive.   In most cases, however, only about 1/2 of the debt is paid off in a comparatively short time, and it would appear that the seal is able to extend the payment over a prolonged period during which the metabolism is only slightly above normal.

It is probably significant that the resting metabolism of seals as determined both by Irving (1938) and by Scholander is much higher than for mammals generally.   Irving gives the average figure 265 ml oxygen per min. for a seal of 29 kg which is more than for a man of 70 kg, and Scholander's results for the same weight vary from 200 ml to 300.   There is reason to suspect therefore that the basal level has not been reached in the experiments, and it appears possible that an oxygen debt can be paid off after a dive without any visible increase in metabolism.

The oxygen debt must be represented in the organism by the accumulation of split products, of which lactic acid is the best known, from the nutritional substances.   In the upper group of curves the results of sampling the arterial blood before, during, and after the dive are summarized.   It is worthy of note that the oxygen in the blood falls to a very low level and recovers within a minute.   The lactic acid shows only a slight rise during the dive and a very considerable one after.   This is a very significant fact to which we shall presently return.   When the total lactic acid present in blood and muscle at the end of a dive is figured out, which can be done only very roughly, it is found to be of the order of 1 g per minute of the dive, or more, which must afterwards be disposed of by combustion and regeneration.   The presence of other split products cannot be excluded, but is not definitely suggested by the results.

The sudden rise in blood lactic acid just after the dive might indicate a suspension or at least a great reduction in blood flow through the muscles during the dive, and the most interesting and probably the most important adjustment taking place in diving is the extreme slowing of the heart rate observed by several authors and amply confirmed by Scholander. The electrocardiogram shown in Fig. 49 illustrates

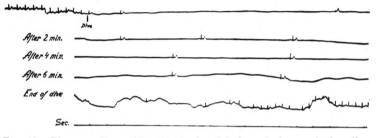

After 2 min.
After 4 min.
After 6 min.
End of dive
Sec.

FIG. 49. Electrocardiographic record of seal before, during, and after dive. (Scholander.)

the point. The rate drops from 120 per min. to about 10. With such a very slow pulse blood pressure cannot possibly be kept up unless the peripheral circulation is largely suspended, and there is reason to believe (Irving, 1938) that at least in muscles and perhaps also in many internal organs the arteries are closed down. A corresponding bradycardia during diving has been observed also in the beaver and in diving birds (Irving, Scholander) but not so far in whales, where a mechanism for shunting blood through the retia mirabilia is suggested by studies made by Eriksson in Scholander's laboratory.

We know from Barcroft's admirable book *The Architecture of Physiological Function* that it is the central nervous system which requires oxygen at a fairly high tension to work properly while all other organs are very resistant, and we may reasonably assume therefore that during diving the blood circulation and oxygen supply are reserved mainly for the brain and medulla.

The mechanisms for prolonged diving turn out to be closely related to those allowing man to contract a large oxygen debt during work, and the maximum debt allowed does not seem to be essentially different when the size of the animals is taken into consideration.   The small animals having a high rate of resting metabolism per unit weight can as a rule contract a debt corresponding only to a few minutes' metabolism, but it must be admitted that the domestic duck will stand 27 minutes' asphyxiation (Richet, 1899).   The maximum debt of a seal weighing 30 kg corresponds to 20–25 minutes.   In man the maximum debt incurred during work corresponds to 40 minutes.   The large whales of 50 to 100 tons can remain submerged for about an hour, and in the case of the sperm whale perhaps more.   After such a dive they will stay near the surface and "blow" at short intervals for some time. The bottlenose, which can stay down for up to two hours, weighs only 8–15 tons.   Although there are large discrepancies there is some relation to size, and the conception of a relation to rate of metabolism is strengthened by the fact that cold-blooded divers will stand submersion for very long periods.

There are certain indications in experiments on man exposed to varied tensions of oxygen during work, and in experiments and observations on diving birds and mammals, that a continuous or intermittent supply of a little oxygen increases the amount of debt which it is possible to contract.   No explanation can be given at present.

The main difference between a diver and a non-diver appears to be in the regulation of the circulation which allows the diver to reduce greatly the blood-flow to the muscles and perhaps also to other organs and to reserve the supply mainly for the central nervous system.

Animals diving to considerable depths have one more serious difficulty to encounter.   It was observed on human beings, diving by means of a helmet or in a "caisson," that unless special precautions were taken they were liable to "caisson disease."   They are supplied with air at a pressure corresponding to the depth, that is, approximately one extra atmosphere for every 10 meters.   Breathing compressed air is not in itself harmful unless the oxygen pressure is raised above

1 atmosphere, but the blood and gradually also the tissues become saturated with the inert "nitrogen" at the high pressure, and when the pressure is reduced by the diver returning to the surface, bubbles of nitrogen may be suddenly released, just as in a soda-water bottle when it is opened.   When sufficient bubbles are released in the blood itself they may block the passage through capillaries and kill the patient, but also the liberation of nitrogen bubbles in nerves and other tissues may give rise to very distressing symptoms.   To guard against this danger it had become customary for divers to ascend with extreme slowness, taking hours to get up from, say, 40 meters. Haldane (1907) introduced the ascent by stages, having found that the pressure could always safely be reduced to about half when equilibrium had been established at a certain pressure. In the lung of a seal or whale making a deep dive the air must become compressed, and it was a mystery why they did not develop caisson disease when staying long at great depths and returning directly to the surface.   This mystery has been cleared up, at least in principle, by Scholander.   In a man in a diving dress the lungs are normally inflated and the circulation through them is normal.   In the diving animals the lungs become greatly reduced in volume by the pressure of the water.   The alveolar surface is therefore reduced and the thickness increased, tending to reduce the rate of nitrogen diffusion so that the animals can attain greater depths and stay down longer without much danger.   The slowing of the blood-flow must further reduce the diffusion, and it is quite possible that only a fraction of the total blood becomes supersaturated and that the nitrogen concentration is rapidly reduced when this is mixed with the rest of the blood.   Scholander points out that the presence of a large "dead space," made up of the trachea and bronchi, further reduces the effective volume and alveolar surface of the lungs, because most and eventually all of the air is transferred to the dead space from which very little diffusion will take place, and he shows that in the diving mammals the lungs can be completely collapsed and all the air transferred to the air passages.

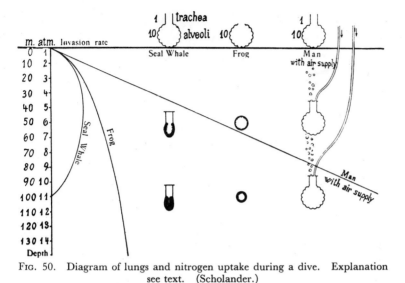

FIG. 50. Diagram of lungs and nitrogen uptake during a dive. Explanation see text. (Scholander.)

This is well brought out in the accompanying diagrams (Fig. 50). The figure to the right illustrates the conditions in the lungs of man breathing all the time in his helmet and discharging air to the surface. The middle figures represent the lung of a diving animal without a dead space (e.g., a frog) at the surface and at the depths of 50 and 100 m, and the left-hand figures represent conditions when there is a dead space having a volume 1/10 of the alveolar. At one hundred meters all the air will be in the dead space and practically no diffusion will take place. The curves give relative rates of nitrogen uptake in the three cases. Quite recently Scholander measured the lungs of fin whales of 22–25 meters length (weighing probably about 70,000 kg). He found them astonishingly small, holding only 1½ to 2 cubic meters of air when inflated to their maximum capacity. The trachea and large bronchi dissected out would hold 150–200 liters or just 1/10 of the lung volume. These whales dive to depths of 300 m or more just after an inspiration. Laurie (1933), who determined the gases dissolved in the blood and urine of a number of blue and fin whales, found only slight supersaturations with nitrogen.

VII

THE RESPIRATORY FUNCTIONS OF BLOOD

In the respiratory organs proper the gases are transported from one medium to another by diffusion and, for all we know, diffusion is also the only mechanism for the transport into and out of the ultimately respiring cells, but in between we have a transport by convection in the flowing blood. The diffusion distances are always short and generally only small fractions of 1 mm. The convection distances can be anything from less than 1 mm to many meters.

The efficiency of the convection transport depends upon several factors. One, which has been touched upon before, is the anatomical arrangements governing the blood-flow. It is essential that the respiratory surfaces should be supplied with "venous" blood, coming directly from the respiring organs, and that the arterialized blood should travel directly back to these, while any mixing of arterial and venous blood greatly reduces the efficiency. Another important factor is the volume flow of blood which must be regulated so as to correspond at any time to the requirements of any particular organ and of the body as a whole. This will be briefly discussed when the third factor, the transport capacity of the blood, which is the main theme of this chapter, has been dealt with.

The transport capacity of a fluid for a gas is determined by the relation between the pressure or "tension" of the gas and the corresponding quantity which the fluid will hold. In pure water this relation is rectilinear and the oxygen quantities corresponding to the possible tensions are so small that water is inadequate as a carrier except in cases of very low metabolism. The absorption coefficient of water for CO_2 being 100% at a temperature of 15.5°C water could serve as a transport medium in many cases. Supposing in an aquatic animal that the CO_2 tension reached the figure of 40 mm in the respiring cells while it was only 2 mm in the surrounding medium, a transport of 5 volumes per cent, corresponding to the tension difference, would be possible.

For reasons which have nothing to do with the transport of gases, pure water is never utilized by animals as an internal medium, and in all the cases with which we have to deal transport takes place by means of substances which combine chemically with the gas in question.   To be of use as a transport mechanism such combination must be "dissociable" in the sense that, at least within a certain range, the combined quantity of gas must increase with increasing gas-tension, making the properties of the combination capable of expression in a "dissociation" curve relating tension to combined quantity.   This will be amply illustrated in the following. It will be convenient to discuss separately first the transport of CO_2 and next the transport of O_2, although the two are to some extent mutually interdependent.

The transport capacity of blood for CO_2.   The fluids actually transporting CO_2 in the animal body have a complicated and varied composition, normally containing strong kations (Na^+) and anions (Cl^-) and also weak anions like phosphate, lactate, and protein ions.   It is not proposed to go into the separate effects of these different ions.   It is sufficient to state that there is generally a surplus of strong kations over strong anions which combines with CO_2 to form bicarbonates and make up the "alkali reserve."   The dissociation range of bicarbonates alone is at very low CO_2 tensions and would in most cases be unsuitable for respiration purposes, but the range is extended by the presence of other weak acids.   When biological fluids, acting as carriers of CO_2, are exposed in "saturators" to atmospheres containing known concentrations of the gas, and the corresponding quantities of CO_2 in 100 volumes of fluid are determined, curves can be constructed relating CO_2 tensions, expressed generally in mm Hg, to quantities in volumes per cent.   Examples of such curves are given in

Fig. 51 from the review given by Florkin (1934) in which the lowest heavy line represents the amount of CO_2 absorbed by water. It will be noted that the blood of the worm *Urechis* absorbs by chemical combination only up to a pressure of about 20 mm; above that the curve becomes parallel to the

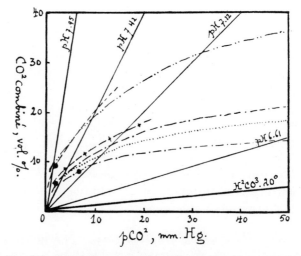

FIG. 51. CO_2 dissociation curves for different bloods compared with sea water represented by lowest heavy line.

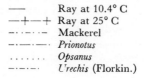

——	Ray at 10.4° C
—+—+	Ray at 25° C
—·—··—	Mackerel
—·——·—·	*Prionotus*
....	*Opsanus*
—·—·—·	*Urechis* (Florkin.)

curve for water and the specific transport capacity is exhausted. The other curves show increases in combined CO_2 up to much higher pressures, outside the range depicted. When the tension is known at which the blood of one of these animals is unloaded with regard to CO_2 in the respiratory organ and also the tension at which CO_2 is taken up in the tissue the transport capacity can be read off from the curve. Conversely if we know the quantities in arterial and venous blood and the unloading tension we can figure out the average CO_2 tension obtaining in the tissues.

Such a calculation is valid only if the balance of acids and bases remains the same during the circulation cycle, and in many cases, probably in a majority, this condition does not hold. The failure may be due to actual variations in the content of ions, but the normal reason, at least in vertebrates, is a shift in the reaction of hæmoglobin by its combination with oxygen. Oxyhæmoglobin is definitely more acid than reduced hæmoglobin and at the same tension arterial blood therefore contains less CO_2 than venous. The difference for man—or rather for the subject J.S.H.—is illustrated in the curves Fig. 52. The thick line represents the actual curve along which the change in CO_2 takes place, provided the oxygen removed by metabolism is replaced with 0.8 volumes of CO_2. A steep curve means a reduced difference in

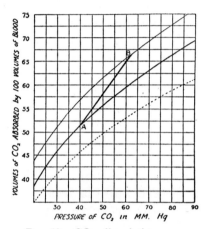
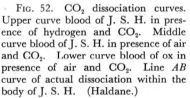

FIG. 52. CO_2 dissociation curves. Upper curve blood of J. S. H. in presence of hydrogen and CO_2. Middle curve blood of J. S. H. in presence of air and CO_2. Lower curve blood of ox in presence of air and CO_2. Line *AB* curve of actual dissociation within the body of J. S. H. (Haldane.)

tension between venous and arterial blood, and facilitates, as Haldane points out, the regulation of the blood p_H.

It does not seem possible at present to correlate in detail the CO_2 absorption curves determined for many different animals with the corresponding œcological conditions.

Generally speaking, gill-breathing, and particularly marine, animals are exposed to media with a very low CO_2 tension of at most a few mm, while the tension in lungs is much higher, ranging up to 50 mm. The former utilize a portion of the curve which is normally quite steep, and they can have low total capacities, as pointed out by Winterstein (1909), and a low content of protein or other weak acids.

The rôle of carbonic anhydrase in CO_2 transport. In 1928 O. Henriques studied the reaction $H_2CO_3 \rightleftharpoons CO_2 + H_2O$, which is a necessary link in the bicarbonate formation in the tissues as well as in the CO_2 elimination from bicarbonate at the respiratory surfaces. He pointed out that according to the kinetic studies of Faurholt (1924) this reaction is a comparatively slow process which could not possibly reach an equilibrium in the second or so during which a blood particle is in contact with respiring cells and alveolar air respectively. He found that CO_2 is given off from blood, but not from a simple bicarbonate solution, with extreme rapidity, and he brought forward evidence to show that the CO_2 in the blood was not in the main present as bicarconate but in a complex combination with hæmoglobin. Later investigations, summarized by Roughton (1935), have shown, however, that the bicarbonate concept is substantially correct, but the reaction is speeded up so as to attain equilibrium in a fraction of a second by an enzyme, carbonic anhydrase, present in the corpuscles. The enzyme was isolated in a highly concentrated form by Meldrum and Roughton (1934). It is present in the red cells of vertebrates, but not related to the hæmoglobin, and has been demonstrated also in many tissues, both in vertebrates and invertebrates. The enzyme may perform an important function in the tissues by catalysing the reaction $CO_2 + H_2O \rightarrow H_2CO_3$, but it is a puzzling fact that it is absent in many cases where one would expect it to be useful, e.g., in many muscles. In certain animals (*Lumbricus, Amphioxus*) it seems to be completely lacking (Brinkman, 1933; H. van Goor, 1937). A fairly high concentration is found in the gills of many marine invertebrates (*Loligo, Limulus, Homarus*, according to Ferguson, Lewis, and Smith, 1937) and fishes (Leiner, 1938), and this seems easy to understand, but Leiner found even more in the pseudobranchia of several fishes where the respiratory function which Leiner postulates is extremely doubtful, because these structures do not come in contact with the surrounding medium and are supplied with arterial blood which goes on to the ipsilateral eye. The function of carbonic anhydrase in this and in many other cases is obscure and worth studying.

One would expect it to be significant that carbonic anhydrase is never found outside cells (Robertson and Ferguson, 1936; van Goor). In vertebrate blood, where the bicarbonate is mainly present in the plasma, the reacting substance H_2CO_3 (or CO_2) must diffuse into the red cells, and the reaction product (CO_2 or H_2CO_3) must diffuse out again. Thanks to the small distances and enormous surfaces there is ample time for this diffusion to take place during the passage through capillaries, but it *seems* an unnecessary complication.

The transport capacity of blood for oxygen. Water is a very poor transport substance for oxygen, because the solubility is quite low (3.4% by volume from an oxygen atmosphere at 15°C) and is even reduced by the presence of dissolved substances. A large number of animals, including all fairly large and highly organized forms so far dealt with, possess special transport substances, combining reversibly with oxygen according to the O_2 tension to which they are exposed. Four groups of such substances are known, all of which are pigments containing a heavy metal. The hæmoglobins, chlorocruorins, and hæmerythrins contain iron, and the hæmocyanins copper. They will be considered here from a biological and only incidentally from a chemical or physicochemical point of view. These have been exhaustively dealt with by Barcroft (1928), L. J. Henderson (1928), Redfield (1933), and Florkin (1934). It will be convenient to deal first with the hæmoglobins which are both the best known and the most interesting respiratory pigments.

Hæmoglobin is a proteid with an iron-containing prosthetic group, hæmatin, in combination with a globulin which definitely differs from one species to another. The unit molecular weight corresponding to 1 atom of iron is, according to Svedberg (1933), 17,250, but hæmoglobins differ greatly in the number of units which the actual molecules contain. In the vertebrates the blood-hæmoglobins contain 4 such units, perhaps with the exception of the *Cyclostomata*. In *Myxine* Svedberg found only 2. Among the invertebrates the larvæ of *Chironomus* have hæmoglobins of 1 unit, certain polychæte worms of 2, but the rest have very large molecules with from 18 to 144 units in each. Each unit can combine with 1 molecule of oxygen or of carbon monoxide.

The occurrence of hæmoglobins in the animal kingdom is very puzzling, and it is necessary to assume that the substance has been evolved independently in many different animal forms, a conception which became easier to entertain when it was shown by Keilin (1925) that derivatives of hæmatin are very widely distributed in animals and present in almost every cell. Pantin (1932) mentions the case of two nearly related species of *Holothuria* (*Cucumaria elongata* and *saxicola*) of which one living in mud possesses hæmoglobin corpuscles while the other does not. He stresses the point that Hb must have been evolved in one step to be at all useful. Outside the vertebrates, in which hæmoglobin is the sole and universal oxygen carrier (lacking only in *Amphioxus* and in the planktonic eel-larvæ, *Leptocephali*), it is found in a number of *Annelida* and *Mollusca*, in several insects and in single representatives of other groups.

In most of the *Invertebrata* hæmoglobin is dissolved in the blood plasma, but in all vertebrates and in some invertebrates it is confined within corpuscles. Hæmoglobin in solution can exist only in rather low concentration without causing a high degree of viscosity and, in case of the smaller Hb-molecules, a high colloid osmotic pressure. Inside corpuscles the hæmoglobin has its own chemical environment which may be of some functional significance (Barcroft, 1922).

The respiratory characteristics of blood containing hæmoglobin (or any other respiratory pigment) can be expressed by (1) the oxygen capacity, and (2) the dissociation curve. The oxygen capacity is the maximum amount of oxygen in volumes per cent with which the blood will combine. The oxygen capacity of the blood in most invertebrates is quite low, ranging from 1 to 2 vols % in most molluscs, from 3 to 10 in

worms and in chironomids.   In fishes, Amphibia, and reptiles
the values given are between 5 and 15, while in the warm-
blooded animals they are usually between 15 and 20, reaching
very high figures, even 40, in the divers.   There is an unmis-
takable correlation between the call for oxygen of an organism
and the oxygen capacity of the blood, but the relations are
by no means clear-cut.

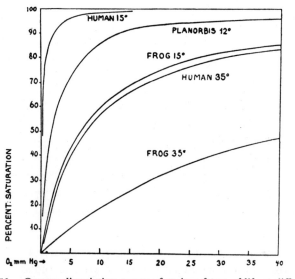

FIG. 53.   Oxygen dissociation curves of various forms of life at different
temperatures.   (Barcroft.)

The affinity of blood or pure hæmoglobins for oxygen is a
complex phenomenon, depending upon a number of conditions, the most important of which are temperature and hydrogen ion concentration.   The affinity is expressed by a dissociation curve or a set of such curves, connecting oxygen tension
in the blood with the percentage saturation of the hæmoglobin.
The curves in Fig. 53 illustrate the remarkable difference in
the dissociation curves of hæmoglobin from different animals,
and give also some indication of the temperature effect, and
the curves in Fig. 54 illustrate the effect of a change in reaction brought about by variations in the CO_2 tension, such as

would be likely to occur in the living organism. It is a significant fact that the effect is very pronounced at low oxygen tensions and practically disappears at full saturation. A brief characterization of the affinity of a certain kind of blood for oxygen which is, however, sufficient for many biological purposes (Krogh and Leitch, 1919), can be given by the tensions of "loading" (t_l) and "unloading" (t_u). The loading tension is defined as the tension which will allow the blood to

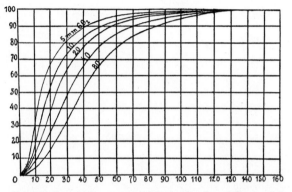

FIG. 54.   Oxygen dissociation curves of dog's blood at different CO_2 tensions. (Krogh.)

become 95% saturated with oxygen, a figure which comes very close to the normal saturation of arterial blood, while the "unloading" tension corresponds to half saturation. This does not mean of course that the blood becomes necessarily half saturated in the passage through the tissues, but is only a convenient way of expressing the relative facility with which oxygen is given off from the hæmoglobin. A high t_u increases availability of the oxygen. In Fig. 53 the t_u of human hæmoglobin at 15°C is about 0.2 mm, while at 38° it is 8 mm. In the actual human blood the t_u is about 30 mm.

Generally the loading and unloading tensions are not independent variables, but a high t_l is associated with a relatively high t_u and vice versa. This means a conflict of interest in the economy of the organism where it is desirable that the t_l is as low as possible to insure saturation in the respiratory organs, and the t_u as high as possible to facilitate the passage of oxygen from the blood to the tissues. The following examples will indicate the compromise struck between the conflicting interests and illustrate the wonderful adaptability of hæmoglobin to meet the different and variable œcological conditions.

When dissociation curves are compared at a standard temperature the differences in t_u are very large, but they become much reduced if each curve is made out for the "normal" temperature of the organism in question, which means in other words that hæmoglobins are adapted to the temperature at which they have normally to function. This is brought out by comparisons between cold-blooded animals from tropical and temperate climates and between the latter and warm-blooded ones, but it would be interesting and instructive to obtain curves for arctic forms which are quite active and have a fairly high metabolism at temperatures about the freezing point.

Respiratory environment and blood characteristics. 1. *Fairly constant environment.* Fishes living in the sea or in rapidly flowing fresh waters which are nearly or completely in diffusion equilibrium with the atmosphere are exposed to a very constant environment with a high oxygen tension of 100–160 mm and a CO_2 tension usually below 1 mm with which the blood is brought into practical equilibrium during its passage through the gills. Such fishes have a high t_l and generally also a fairly high t_u at the summer temperature to which the fish is normally exposed. Cases in point are the cod, plaice, and trout at 14–17°C (studied by Krogh and Leitch, 1919), mackerel, sea-robin, and toadfish at 20° (Root, 1931), skate at 10° (Dill, Edwards, and Florkin, 1932) and certain freshwater fishes, paku, bassara, and haimara, living in rapid streams in the tropics and studied by Willmer at 28–30°C (1934). It is a very interesting fact that in all these fishes CO_2 has a profound influence on the affinity of the blood for oxygen which is manifest and even pronounced at high O_2

tensions, so that exposure to CO_2 at a pressure of 10 mm or less will increase the loading tension greatly.   The curve (Fig. 55) shows the effect on the paku.   The CO_2 effect on the tension of unloading is of course beneficial, while the effect on the loading tension cannot become manifest in nature.   Green and Root (1933) showed further that above a certain concentration of CO_2, or any other acid, saturation with oxygen could

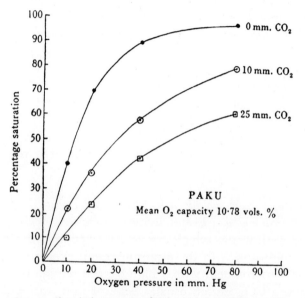

FIG. 55.   Oxygen dissociation curves of paku blood at different CO_2 tensions. (Willmer.)

not be reached at all in several marine fishes.   In a toadfish at p_H 6.5 the maximum saturation obtained at all O_2 tensions above 200 mm would correspond to 49% only of the oxygen capacity.   The biological significance of this remarkable effect is not clear.   It is suggested that it may have something to do with the liberation of oxygen in the "gas gland" of the swimming bladder.   This suggestion is very plausible, but even if proved would not go very far to explain the process of gas secretion in this organ.

In the higher vertebrates including most reptiles, birds, and mammals, but excluding the diving forms, the respiratory environment is also on the whole fairly constant, although some exceptions will be dealt with below, but differs significantly from that of the fishes discussed above. The air in the lungs contains normally about 15% oxygen, corresponding to a pressure of 100–110 mm and 5–6% CO_2 or about 40 mm pressure. In these the CO_2 effect on the O_2 dissociation curve of the blood is on the whole smaller, and very definitely reduced or abolished (Scott, 1938) at the normal loading tensions.

There are distinct differences in the dissociation curves between different species and also within the species, differences which cannot so far be correlated with œcological factors. The birds so far examined (Wastl und Leiner, 1931; Christensen and Dill, 1935) have definitely lower loading and unloading tensions. This is probably correlated with the very high rates of metabolism during flight, but the high body temperature of birds (42°C) may also have something to do with it.

Of the exceptions, alluded to above, from the general rule of a fairly constant respiratory environment, one is concerned with a definite period in the life of each individual, viz. the fœtal life, while the other concerns those individuals which habitually or occasionally visit high altitudes. It will be convenient to deal with these in this place.

The oxygen transport in fœtal blood. During development of the fœtus both in mammals (J. Barcroft and others, 1935) and in birds (F. G. Hall, 1935) the available amount of oxygen appears to be a limiting factor for the rate of growth. In the mammal, oxygen has to diffuse in the placental vessels from the maternal to the fœtal blood which involves in all cases a definite fall in tension. In birds' eggs (and reptile eggs), oxygen must diffuse through the shell and membranes before reaching the blood, and this requires a considerable pressure head. The fœtal blood shows a definitely steeper dissociation curve than the blood of the mother, which has turned out to be due to the presence of a different hæmoglobin. It is well known that the mechanism of hæmoglobin for-

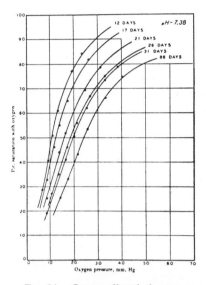

mation in the fœtus differs from that in the mature animal, hæmoglobin being formed in the fœtus along with the blood vessels, but later only in the bone marrow, and it appears that the gradual change in dissociation curve shown in Fig. 56 can be explained by assuming that fœtal hæmoglobin is slowly replaced by the mature kind. The fœtal hæmoglobin is definitely adapted to the peculiar conditions of fœtal life.

Fig. 56. Oxygen dissociation curves of hæmoglobin from chicks during development, at p_H 7.38. Age expressed as from the beginning of incubation. (Hall.)

Adaptation of the blood to high altitudes. A few mammals, especially the llama and vicuna (*Lama huanachus* and *vicugna*), and some birds (*Chlœphaga melanoptera* and *Rhea americana*) live habitually at high altitudes. These were carefully studied by Hall, Dill, and Barron (1936) and the dissociation curves showed a distinct shift towards the left as compared with their low altitude relatives (Fig. 57).

Several other warm-blooded animals, including man, are exposed to low oxygen pressures when occasionally ascending to high altitudes, and the corresponding adaptations have been extensively studied in man. Keys (1938), who has given a very good summary of the literature, estimates that about 10 million humans live permanently at heights above 3,000 m, but only a few hundred above 5,000 m.

Whether the stay at high altitude is of short or of lifelong duration, the adaptation is *not* brought about by any shift in the dissociation curve of the blood, which shortly after birth seems to become an individual constant.   The mechanism is more indirect and gives room for large personal differences.

Above a certain altitude the oxygen pressure in the lungs is insufficient to saturate the blood, and this brings about, partly perhaps through the formation of fixed acids, but probably in a more intricate way, an increase in ventilation which is, however, of very different extent in different individuals. Those individuals who promptly respond by a large increase show the greatest resistance in the acute exposure to low oxygen pressures. The breakdown occurs at nearly the same alveolar oxygen pressure in all cases.

The increased ventilation reduces the CO_2 pressure in the alveoli, and CO_2 is gradually washed out from the blood and tissues whereby the blood is made more alkaline. In the process of acclimatization this is compensated by a corresponding decrease in

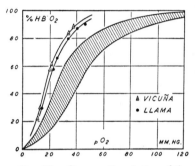

Fig. 57.   Oxygen dissociation of the llama and vicuña at body temperature (39°C) and p_H 7.1, compared with the range for eight lowlanders including man, horse, and dog.   (Hall, Dill and Barron.)

the "alkali reserve."   Assuming a constant metabolism, the amount of CO_2 liberated in the tissues will therefore bring about a larger increase in acidity and thereby raise the actual tension of unloading, a very beneficial adaptation.

The rate of circulation during rest or corresponding to a well-defined amount of work does not change appreciably, but the oxygen capacity of the blood increases gradually during a couple of months by the formation of new red corpuscles.   The final capacity is closely correlated with the altitude and reaches at 5,300 m an average of 29.2 vols. %, distributed over 7.3 million red corpuscles per cubic millimeter (Keys, 1938).

In dogs born and reared at high altitudes, Hurtado and collaborators (1937, quoted from Dill, 1938) have found also a very considerable increase in muscle hæmoglobin over that found in dogs at sea level.   It would be interesting to learn whether such an increase can be brought about in mature individuals.

The amount of work which can be performed by a fully acclimatized person decreases with increasing height and is a function of the maximum amount of oxygen which can be obtained by the most violent ventilation.   As seen from the

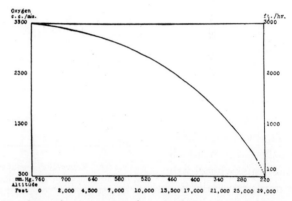

FIG. 58.   Approximate amount of oxygen that a man can obtain and utilize for climbing (ordinate right) at all altitudes between sea level and the summit of Mount Everest.   (Y. Henderson.)

accompanying graph, reproduced from a very instructive recent summary by Y. Henderson (1939), the power of climbing is reduced to 0 below the summit of Mount Everest. Acclimatization to high altitudes does not improve the power for work at sea level, but reduces it, because the lowered alkali reserve will demand a more rapid circulation and a larger ventilation to eliminate the same amount of CO_2 without unduly acidifying the blood.

Variable environments.   On pp. 10, 14 it was set forth in some detail that the air in the upper strata of the soil and many temperate fresh waters may occasionally show very low oxygen concentrations, while in tropical swamps the low oxygen may be further complicated by rather high CO_2 tensions. The hæmoglobins of many animals show characteristic adaptations to these conditions. The blood of the carp, pike, and eel was found to have at 15°C a t_1 of about 10 mm and a t_u at a very low CO_2 tension (0.3 mm) of 2–3 mm (Krogh and

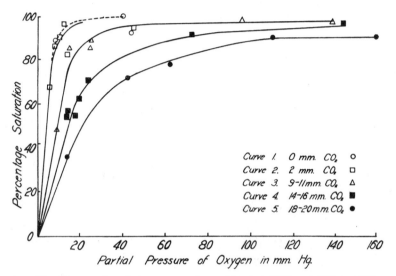

FIG. 59. Oxygen dissociation curves of carp blood at 15°C and different CO_2 tensions. (Black and Irving.)

Leitch, 1919; Black and Irving, 1937). This would make the transfer of oxygen to the tissues extremely difficult were it not that the CO_2 effect is very large and may raise the t_u to 6 mm (at 7.5 mm CO_2) and probably beyond. Black and Irving found a t_u at 18–20 mm CO_2 tension of not less than 25 mm (Fig. 59). These adaptations enable the fishes to live in very poor water which would be rapidly fatal, e.g., to trout.

Certain invertebrates possessing hæmoglobin utilize the pigment only at low oxygen tensions, while diffusion and transport in simple solution is sufficient at higher tensions. This point is brought out when the hæmoglobin is put out of function by exposing the animals to a low concentration of carbon monoxide (7 mm) which saturates the blood, but does not otherwise interfere with the metabolism or activity.

The fresh-water snail *Planorbis corneus*, which frequents stagnant pools and often stays for hours at the bottom, has a blood volume amounting to 1/2 of the weight, containing Hb with an oxygen capacity of 1 to 1.5 vols. %. The snail comes to the surface occasionally and takes air into the lung, but it can also utilize dissolved O_2 through the skin and a functional "gill" (Leitch, 1916; Borden, 1931; Wolvekamp, 1932). The inactivation of the Hb made no difference down to tensions of about 50 mm, but at lower tensions the Hb came definitely into use. Its t_u is at 20° and without CO_2 about 6 mm.

The common earthworm (*Lumbricus*) was studied by similar methods by Dolk and van der Paauv (1929) with very similar results. The hæmoglobin does not come into use until the O_2 pressure is reduced to 55 mm and can maintain an adequate supply down to less than 20 mm. Even at 3 mm 50% of the normal metabolism can be obtained.

The holothurian *Caudina* and the bivalve *Anadara* (*Arca*) have hæmoglobin containing corpuscles which are utilized at rather low tensions, 8–10 mm, according to Kawamoto (1928).

Isabella Leitch (1916) also studied the blood of red *Chironomus* larvæ which have the steepest dissociation curve so far observed. At 20° the t_u is about 0.2 mm and there is a definite CO_2 effect reducing the saturation at 0.2 mm O_2 and 8 mm CO_2 to 39%. These larvæ live like the *Tubifex* worms mentioned on p. 30 in vertical tubes built from the muddy bottom of lakes and ponds where the oxygen tension is normally low and may become reduced to 0. It can be observed directly when the transparent larvæ are viewed through a microspectroscope that the hæmoglobin does not begin to function until the O_2 tension in the surrounding water is below 7 mm. Pause (1919) found that red larvæ of *Chironomus gregarius* could live in water with 0.2 ml O_2/l (corresponding to a tension of 4–5 mm), but were killed in a few days at lower tensions.   In their natural habitats the *Chiro-nomid* larvæ can stand much lower oxygen tensions and per-haps even complete oxygen lack (Juday, 1908), probably by changing over partially or completely to anaerobic me-tabolism (Harnisch, 1936).

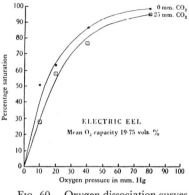

Willmer (1934) describes the very peculiar situation of fishes in tropical swamps in British Guiana. The oxygen is so low (and often practically absent) that the fishes have had to develop accessory organs for breath-ing air.   At the same time they are exposed to water with a CO_2 tension which is sometimes very high.   In

Fig. 60.   Oxygen dissociation curves for blood of electric eel at CO_2 tensions from 0 to 25 mm.   (Willmer.)

these circumstances their dissociation curves are not very steep, but the CO_2 effect is very much reduced (Fig. 60).

In one fish, the yarrow (*Erythrinus*), Willmer studied the complex relations between the gas content of the water and

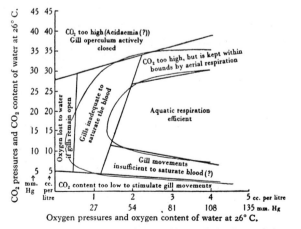

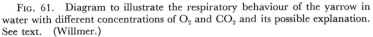

Fig. 61.   Diagram to illustrate the respiratory behaviour of the yarrow in water with different concentrations of O_2 and CO_2 and its possible explanation. See text.   (Willmer.)

the mode of respiration.   His results are illustrated in Fig. 61. Between the two curved lines the respiration was mixed, while outside them it was purely aërial and inside purely aquatic.   The most interesting point is that aërial respiration is resorted to at low CO_2 tensions, even when the oxygen content of the water is high.   This appears to show that CO_2 at tensions from about 10 to about 25 mm is necessary as a stimulus to branchial respiration, an adaptation which is probably unique among fishes and foreshadows regulation mechanisms in much higher forms.   Adaptation to œcological conditions is evidently specific and of very little value as a character of larger systematic groups.

Hæmoglobin as an oxygen store.   In all cases where hæmoglobin is present in tissue cells and does not circulate at all the only function which can at present be assigned to it is to act as a store of oxygen on which the tissue can draw when the supply from the blood fails or is inadequate.   This will usually involve the assumption that the tissue hæmoglobin is normally saturated with oxygen and shows a steeper dissociation curve than the hæmoglobin of the blood.   The studies of H. Theorell (1934) have shown this to be the case.   The t_u of horse-muscle hæmoglobin is 3.6 mm, and Theorell points out further that the effect of CO_2 or acidity is very slight and that this may have something to do with the fact that in muscles it may be exposed to larger variations than in the blood.   This reasoning is valid only when we assume that the time factor is important in the utilization of the oxygen store.   The distribution of myoglobin is curious.   It seems always to be present in the heart.   It is generally present in skeletal muscles in higher vertebrates, but absent in fishes (one exception noted by Ray Lankester is the muscles of the dorsal fin of *Hippocampus*).   The concentration varies greatly.   As mentioned on p. 81 it is very high in diving mammals and probably also at high altitudes (p. 102). It appears to increase with age, as indicated by the difference in colour between veal and beef.   It is generally higher in wild animals than in tame of the same species, but it is nearly absent from the powerful flight muscles of most birds. The storage function of myoglobin is probably of importance in static contractions when the blood supply becomes inadequate (Lindhard, 1920) and it may also have to function rhythmically in the ordinary process of contraction.

Ray Lankester (1872) made a very extensive and careful study of the distribution of hæmoglobin and found it in many unexpected places. While it is otherwise absent from smooth muscle it is present in the rectal muscles of man and probably other mammals. It is present also in the pharynx and radula muscles of gastropods (observed in *Limnæa, Paludina, Littorina, Patella, Chiton, Aplysia*) and in the pharyngeal tube of the worm *Aphrodite*. In all these cases the concentration is rather low, but in the chain of nerve ganglia of *Aphrodite* it is high enough to give the colour of mammalian blood. About the function in these locations we can only make guesses.

Fig. 62.   Part of the red organ in a young *Gastrophilus* larva.   Probably ca. 60/1.
(Prenant.)

Certain insect larvæ (*Gastrophilus*) living in the stomach of mammals, especially in the horse, have a peculiar organ made up of large red cells (Fig. 62) which contain hæmoglobin in fairly high concentration and are arranged on tracheal branches which supply them with a large number of tracheoles. The animal must be exposed to periods of oxygen lack, and there can be no reasonable doubt that the organ functions as an oxygen store, although the authors do not appear to entertain this possibility (Prenant, 1900; v. Kemnitz, 1917).

It is a very remarkable fact that quite similar organs occupy one-fourth to one-half of the abdomen in one European (*Anisops*) and one American genus (*Buenoa*) of *Notonectidæ*. The authors describing these organs (Poisson, 1926; Bare, 1928) were unable to find any plausible function, but the cases would probably repay a closer study from a physiological point of view.

In certain animals the storage of oxygen in the blood itself appears to be of biological importance. The first example to be studied in any detail (by J. Barcroft and H. Barcroft, 1924) was the worm *Arenicola*, burrowing in sand and mud flats in the tidal zone, where during the ebb the access to oxygen is very limited and there is even the danger that the gas may diffuse away from the burrow into the surrounding mud. This danger is minimized by the very steep dissociation curve of the blood. It was clearly shown in this case that the total oxygen capacity of the very large blood volume would be of definite assistance in tiding over the period of inadequate supply, but not sufficient to cover the normal requirements.

This was confirmed by Mabel Borden (1931) who showed further that also *Planorbis* can draw to an œcologically significant extent upon the oxygen stored in its hæmoglobin. Hazelhoff (Jordan, 1922) compared the O_2 content in the lung of *Planorbis* with that of the hæmocyanin containing *Limnæa* when both were kept under water for three hours. In *Limnæa* the oxygen fell off in an hour to the low value of 6% and the metabolism became much reduced. In *Planorbis* the O_2 took 150 minutes to reach 4% and the metabolism was kept up, thanks to the storage function of the hæmoglobin (Fig. 63).

A similar reasoning holds for the echiuroid worm *Urechis caupo*, which works on the whole at somewhat higher oxygen tensions, according to Redfield and Florkin (1931). *Urechis* is exposed to a deficient oxygen supply during low tide, and even when the flats are covered it may occasionally suspend

respiration and live on its oxygen store.   In the case of these
and probably several other animals it is not possible to
distinguish sharply between the transport function and the
storage function of hæmoglobin, but it can be stated generally
that in cases where the total oxygen capacity of the blood in an
invertebrate is high compared with its metabolism there is
reason to suspect a storage function.

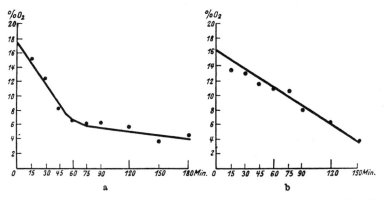

Fig. 63.   Decrease in oxygen content in lungs of *Limnæa stagnalis* and *Planorbis*
corneus when kept under water.   (Hazelhoff.)

A storage function of a definitely rhythmic character is
described by Lindroth (1938) for *Nereis virens* and will probably be discovered also in other animals.   *Nereis* burrows in
sand which is practically oxygen-free.   It will make respiratory movements for about 5 minutes and then keep quiet for
20–30 minutes during which the oxygen in the blood will be
used up and in addition some oxygen debt incurred which
provides the stimulus for the next ventilation period.   During
the non-ventilating periods the blood is withdrawn from the
respiratory appendages and the whole circulation reduced.
The oxygen transport during this period is largely brought
about by diffusion, while the loading of the hæmoglobin is
greatly assisted by circulation.

Hæmocyanins are found in the blood of a majority of molluscs
and crustaceans and in some arachnomorphs including

Limulus, but not so far outside these groups. They contain copper and show in the oxidized state a blue colour which disappears on removal of the oxygen. According to Begemann (1924) they combine with oxygen in the proportion of 1 atom of Cu to 1 of oxygen, while hæmoglobin takes up 2 atoms of oxygen for each atom of iron. The unit molecular weight is equal to that of hæmoglobin, but the actual molecules are very large, containing from 36 to 288 units (Svedberg, 1933). Hæmocyanin is always present in solution. The oxygen capacities of hæmocyanin bloods are never very high, varying from a fraction of 1% in many bivalves, gastropods, and crustaceans to a maximum of 5% in the very active cephalopods. The dissociation curves are very similar to those for hæmoglobins and almost as variable among themselves, but it would appear that the temperature effect is less pronounced and extremely steep curves, adapted to very low oxygen tensions, have not so far been observed. The following table compiled from papers by Winterstein (1909), Wolvekamp (1932, 1938), Redfield, Coolidge, and Hurd (1926), Begemann (1924), Redfield and Ingalls (1933), shows some characteristics of hæmocyanin-containing bloods. In some respects

TABLE 10

RESPIRATORY CHARACTERISTICS OF HÆMOCYANIN-CONTAINING BLOODS

	O_2 capacity vols %	Tp	CO_2 tension mm	mm O_2 t_u	t_l	mm O_2 t_l
Octopus	4–5	25°	0.6	3	15	Strong
Sepia		25°	2.3	14	45	—
Loligo	3.5–4	23°	0.5	36	90	—
Helix	0.8	20°	0.5	6	25	Slight
Busycon	1.5–3	22°	0.5	12	55	Inversed
Limulus	0.9–1.5	23°	0.5	11	40	Inversed
Crustacea		23°	0.5	12	35	Strong

these have a definite œcological significance, but others are from this point of view obscure. The very active squids (*Loligo*) living in the open sea have a high loading tension.

Thanks to the pronounced effect of CO_2 they utilize 80% or more of the oxygen capacity, but the uptake of oxygen in the gills will be seriously affected even by a few mm CO_2 pressure. *Octopus* which often hides in narrow crevices in rocky shores can stand fairly low oxygen tensions, and the same is the case with *Limulus* and the gastropod *Busycon*. The inversion of the CO_2 effect in these latter forms is one of the obscure points. The *Crustacea* examined were found to have identical dissociation curves.

Chlorocruorins are found dissolved in the blood of serpulid worms as a burgundy-red pigment of very nearly the same colour in the oxidized and reduced state. They were studied in several genera including *Myxicola*, *Spirographis* and *Sabella* by H. Munro Fox (1926, 1932). The pigments have very large molecules, contain iron and are related to hæmoglobins, from which however they show very pronounced differences. Fox found the oxygen affinity so low that the blood of *Spirographis* and some others could not even become fully saturated in contact with atmospheric air. The oxygen capacity of *Spirographis* blood was found to be 9.1 vols % in air and 10.2 in oxygen. The dissociation curves are affected in the same general way by temperature and CO_2 as most hæmoglobins, and they combine with CO for which the affinity is higher than for O_2. The chlorocruorins are efficient carriers of oxygen at relatively high pressures (unloading tensions from 10 to 25 mm), but not adapted to the low tensions to which the animals must be exposed when retiring into their tubes.

Hæmerythrins are found only in corpuscles in the cœlomic fluids of the class of sipunculoid worms, and appear to be present in all the species belonging to this small group to the exclusion of any other respiratory pigment. According to Florkin (1933) they contain iron, but are not closely related to the hæmoglobins. They are stated to combine with oxygen in the curious relation of 1 mole of O_2 to 3 atoms of Fe and do not combine with CO.   The dissociation curve for O_2 is fairly steep (t_u about 8 mm, at $19°C$) and CO_2 has no effect.

The oxygen capacity of the hæmerythrin in the cœlomic fluid of *Sipunculus* is quite low, 1.6 vols. % on an average, but the quantity of fluid is very large, and it would appear that the pigment acts mainly as a store of oxygen to be utilized in adverse conditions in the marine mud in which the animal lives.

The adaptation of the circulation to respiratory needs.   The rate of blood flow is evidently of no less importance for the transport of the gases than the transport capacity, but unfortunately very little is known about it, except in the case of man and a few mammals.   For these it has been shown that the adaptation of the circulation to the varying respiratory demands is of the same order of importance and perfection as the adaptation of the lung ventilation.   The following points are noteworthy and probably applicable to a very large number of forms besides the few for which they have been definitely ascertained.

Increased activity of an organ demands and secures an increase in the blood-flow through that particular organ. This increase, which is brought about mainly by relaxation of arteries and especially of arterioles, is always correlated with a dilatation of capillaries and in many cases, especially in muscles during work, with an opening up of a large number of capillaries previously closed as described in the writer's monograph on *The Anatomy and Physiology of Capillaries* (Revised ed. 1929).   The number of open capillaries may increase more than tenfold, and the utilization of the oxygen supplied through the arterial blood may increase from the usual 33% to about 90%.   An increase in flow to a single organ is to some extent compensated by a restriction of the flow to the others, but it is the general rule that it involves an increase in the total circulation through the lungs as measured by the "minute volume" of the right heart.   In man this minute volume is of the order of 4–5 l during rest in a reclining posi-

tion.   During the heaviest sustained work in young athletic
men, involving an oxygen consumption of 4 l/m, it may reach
the astonishing figure of 35 l/m with an oxygen unsaturation
in the venous blood of 120 ml/l or 70% of the arterial saturation (E. H. Christensen, 1931).   This means that in the
venous blood from the active muscles the oxygen concentration must be definitely lower than 50 ml/l.   Corresponding
figures are not available for any other organism.   The influence of activity upon the local and general circulation in some
lower forms both vertebrate and invertebrate would be well
worth studying.

VIII

TRACHEAL RESPIRATION

THE tracheal respiration as found within the *Arthropoda* in the groups *Onychophora* (*Peripatus*), *Solifugæ* (Bernard, 1895), *Phalangidæ*, some *Acarina*, *Myriapoda*, *Chilopoda*, and *Insecta* represents a solution of the problem of providing oxygen to the cells, different in principle from the mechanisms so far discussed, a solution which allows a high degree of organization to be attained, but which sets rather narrow limits to the possible size.

The tracheæ are air-filled tubes originating from special openings in the integument, the "spiracles," and by repeated branching reaching out to all parts of the body and ofter penetrating into the very cells, thus obviating the convection by a circulating fluid.

There is no hard and fast line of distinction between tracheal and pulmonary respiration. In many *Arachnidæ* we find reduced tracheal systems acting mainly as lungs supplying the blood (p. 57). Even in the tracheates proper a circulating blood fulfils other necessary functions of distribution and cannot avoid transporting some oxygen and a larger amount of CO_2. In several insects (Larvæ of *Hypoderma* and *Tipulidæ*, Walter, 1922; Gerbig, 1913) we find a rich supply of tracheoles floating in the blood and very probably supplementing as a kind of lung the direct supply of the tissues. The supply of oxygen obtainable in this way must be limited, however, because the blood does not contain any respiratory pigment and there can be no separation of "arterial" from "venous" blood. The blood-flow moreover is usually rather slow. It might be worth while, however, to study the oxygen tension and the oxygen-carrying capacity of the blood in the large Tipulid larvæ. The CO_2-carrying capacity of the blood is much larger because bicarbonates are regularly present

(Maluf, 1939), and the integument is responsible in many insects for a definite fraction of the CO_2 elimination amounting sometimes to 1/4, even in forms with a highly developed tracheal system.

The structure of tracheal systems shows a very wide range of variations, and many structural peculiarities are far from being understood from an œcological or physiological point of view. It is possible, however, to correlate certain broad structural features with the function and to arrange the tracheal respiratory mechanisms according to a system, however provisional. Tracheal respiration must have been evolved on land and the tracheates are mainly terrestrial, but quite a number of forms have secondarily adopted an aquatic existence and have had their respiratory mechanisms modified in various ways. In the terrestrial forms we can make a distinction be-

FIG. 64. Injection preparation of tracheal system of *Cossus* larva. About natural size. (Krogh.)

tween those forms for which an exchange of gases by diffusion is sufficient and those which have recourse to mechanical ventilation.

Tracheal respiration by diffusion. In a large number of tracheates the tracheal system is arranged (at least in principle) on the system shown in Fig. 64. From a number of spiracles symmetrically arranged along the sides of the body a number of tracheæ branch out to the organs in the corresponding segment or segments. The spiracles are connected lengthwise by tracheal tubes, but these are of secondary importance only. The tracheæ are circular in cross section with chitinous walls fortified by a spiral fold as shown in Fig. 65. They branch fairly regularly and the aggregate cross section remains very nearly constant in the repeated branchings. The finest chitinous branches are continued in extremely numerous and narrow "tracheoles" which are non-chitinous. All the tracheæ are very resistant against pressure, which will produce only a slight shortening of the stems and branches. In these animals there are no specific respiratory movements, and the pressures set up in the body fluids by locomotion or even by violent struggling can cause ventilations only which are too small to be significant.

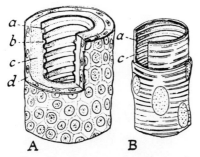

FIG. 65. Structure of tracheae. *A*, close to spiracle. *B*, small branch more highly magnified. *a* epicuticle with spiral folds, *d* epithelial matrix. (Weber.)

When the average length of the tracheæ and their aggregate cross section is made out it becomes possible to calculate the pressure difference necessary for a certain amount of oxygen, corresponding to the metabolism of the animal, to diffuse from the atmosphere to the tracheoles. Measurements made on the tracheal system of a large *Cossus* larva gave an aggregate cross-sectional area of all the tracheæ supplying the tissues of 6.7 mm² with an average length of 6 mm. Through a tube of these dimensions the oxygen necessary for the animal's metabolism, viz., 0.3 mm³/second, will diffuse by a pressure difference of 11 mm,[1] which means that diffusion is ample to

[1] The diffusion rate for CO_2 in air is slightly lower, and the same quantity would require a pressure difference of 13 mm. The CO_2 produced is on an average somewhat less than the oxygen used up, and 10 to 25% are eliminated through the skin. The actual pressure difference in the tracheal system necessary for the transport of CO_2 is therefore rather lower than that for O_2.

meet the call for oxygen even during muscular exertions. This result, which was controlled and secured in several ways (Krogh, 1920.2), can be shown to be valid for a large number of tracheates.

This comes out clearly when the influence of size is considered. The animal under discussion had a length of 60 mm and weighed 3.4 g. Assuming all linear dimensions multiplied by 10, the tracheæ would be 60 mm long with a cross section of 6.7 cm². These dimensions would provide for 10 times the diffusion found, but the animal's weight would increase 1,000 times and the metabolism at least 100 times. Diffusion would be quite inadequate. Conversely conditions would be greatly improved in an animal having 1/10 the linear dimensions (6 mm long) which is much nearer the general size of insects than the *Cossus* larva studied.

The animals which show no respiratory movements and in which the whole of the gas transport takes place by diffusion in the tracheæ are mainly the following: the *Onychophora* (*Peripatus*), the tracheate *Arachnoidea*, *Myriapoda*, and *Chilopoda*, almost all terrestrial insect larvæ, all pupæ and a very large number of *small* imagines. Many imagines have such a high rate of metabolism, especially during flight, that a diffusion transport becomes inadequate when the weight reaches about 0.1 g or perhaps even less. The house fly weighing about 15–20 mg is supposed never to make respiratory movements, but the bee, weighing 100 mg, does so regularly.

Many insects, even fairly large ones like the cockroach (*Periplaneta orientalis*) or the walking stick (*Dixippus morosus*), do not use their ability to make respiratory movements until their metabolism rises above a certain point, either as a result of muscular movements or at rest under the influence of a high temperature. Up to that point the gas exchange is brought about by diffusion only, and it is the rule that the rate of diffusion is definitely cut down by regulation so as to require a larger pressure difference.

The supply of oxygen to the long legs in several insects presents difficulties, and the oxygen concentration in their tracheæ may become very low (Krogh, 1912). In the harvestmen (*Opiliones*) there are special spiracles on the tibiæ of the long legs (H. J. Hansen, 1893).

The *Gastrophilus* larva was mentioned on p. 107 where an account is given of its hæmoglobin-storing cells. These cells are connected with the spiracles through 4 relatively enormous tracheæ (Portier, 1911, p. 318). The air, to which the larvæ will have access only occasionally, is probably very poor in oxygen.

Diffusion regulation. Diffusion of gases in air in a system of rigid tubes would seem to be a process not readily lending itself to regulation on the part of the organism. Nevertheless mechanisms are present at both ends of the tracheæ providing a very effective adaptation of the diffusion to the requirements of the moment.

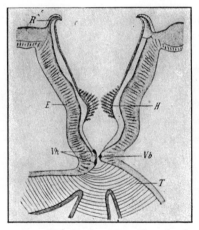

FIG. 66. Section through spiracle of *Cossus* larva. *H* hair filter, *Vh-Vb* closing mechanism. (Claus.)

The spiracles through which the tracheæ communicate with the outside air are as a rule not simple openings, but more or less complex organs sui generis. A comparatively simple type of spiracle is shown in the somewhat diagrammatic Fig. 66. The rim and funnel of the spiracle cannot be wetted by water, which is thus prevented from entering the tracheæ. The hairs at E form a very effective filter preventing the entrance of dust,[1] and finally we have at Vh–Vb a mechanism provided with

[1] A large diversity of spiracle types is found among tracheate insects, and several of the structural traits are probably of respiratory significance.

In the larvæ of the lamellicorn beetles living in earth or manure the spiracles appear closed by a thin membrane, at one time supposed to be continuous, but in reality pierced by numerous exceedingly minute openings. These will provide a very effective filter and in spite of their small aggregate area offer, like

a muscle by which the size of the opening can be regulated and even completely closed. Closing mechanisms are of several different types and in some cases, including the large cockroaches, they are labiate and make up the very outside opening where they can be easily observed. This fact was utilized by Hazelhoff, who in 1926 published a beautiful study of their function.

Hazelhoff found that in the animal at complete rest the spiracles would remain closed at all temperatures up to about 26°C, while at higher temperatures they are opened more and more. Special experiments, in which the animals were subjected to sudden pressure variations in the surrounding atmosphere, showed however that some air could pass between the closed lips. Any struggling on the part of the confined cockroach caused the spiracles to open up after a latent period of a few seconds, and when the struggling ceased they would close, again after a few seconds. Experiments with varied atmospheres showed clearly that the spiracles react to CO_2 and only indirectly and feebly to oxygen lack. One per cent CO_2 has a perceptible effect; with 2% the spiracles are kept permanently open, and with 3% they are widely open. Further experiments in which single spiracles were exposed to a jet of air with or without a suitable concentration of CO_2 were conclusive in showing that the spiracles react by a kind of local reflex to the CO_2 concentration and that the organs which are sensitive to CO_2 are situated just inside the spiracle lips. Similar experiments were made on a number of different insects and spiders, and always with the same result in such forms which permanently or temporarily ventilate by diffusion only.

The regulation mechanism in a flea (*Xenopsylla cheopis*) was carefully studied by Wigglesworth (1935) and found to differ

the stomata in plant leaves, only the slightest resistance against diffusion, which through sufficiently narrow openings in a thin membrane is proportional not to the area but to the circumference. This fact also explains why extremely narrow slits in several types of spiracles can allow a sufficient diffusion of gases.

Inside such openings, which themselves constitute an efficient filter, there is often a very dense felt-like covering of hairs on the spiracle wall, the significance of which remains obscure.

essentially from that of larger insects, a fact which appears to be correlated both with the small absolute size and with the, even relatively, small capacity of the tracheal system.

Most of the spiracles remain closed when no processes requiring extra oxygen are in progress in the corresponding segment, but the third thoracic and eighth abdominal maintain a regular rhythm opening slightly and closing completely several times per minute. This rhythm is affected both by lack of oxygen and by excess CO_2. At a CO_2 pressure of 15 mm (2% in air) the spiracles remain permanently open. Wigglesworth shows that there are no local receptors sensitive to CO_2, and his analysis of a large number of experiments leads to the conclusion that the acidity of the tissues is the main regulating factor. This contention is proved, to my satisfaction at least, by a very ingenious experiment in which a flea was enclosed under the microscope in a small air space surrounded by alkaline pyrogallol absorbing both CO_2 and O_2. In these conditions which involve the production of lactic acid in the tissues all the spiracles remained permanently open, and on readmission of air after 20 minutes asphyxia it took several minutes before any of them began to close, and 20 minutes before the rhythm was normal.

In the hedgehog flea, Herford (1938) found that the oval main tracheæ would begin to collapse during each period of closure, showing that the closing mechanism is air-tight.

The closing mechanism and its reaction to CO_2 in low concentration was demonstrated even in a tick, *Ornithodorus*, by K. Mellanby (1935).

The œcological significance of the diffusion regulation is to be sought, as maintained by Hazelhoff and confirmed by Wigglesworth, in the reduction of water loss. The exchange of gases is not reduced, but will require a steeper concentration gradient when the passage is obstructed and, provided the atmosphere inside the tracheal system remains saturated with water vapour, the diffusion of this vapour to the outside and the consequent loss of water is definitely reduced. Investigations by Buxton (1930), Gunn (1933), and K. Mellanby (1935) show how important it is for many insects to keep down the water loss, demonstrate the increase when the spiracles are forced open, and point out the almost complete impermeability of the integument of many insects to water vapour.

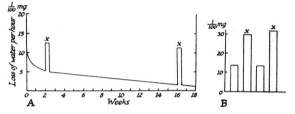

FIG. 67.   The effect of opening the spiracles on the rate of loss of water. *A*, rate of loss from a starving mealworm; *B*, rate of loss from a number of fleas in 1/100 mg per mg per hour.   Columns marked *x* obtained when the spiracles were kept open with 5% CO_2.   (Mellanby.)

The experiment illustrated by Fig. 67 is very convincing. The curve shows the rate of water loss from a fasting mealworm over 18 weeks.   It is gradually reduced with the falling metabolism, but when the animal was forced by CO_2 to keep its spiracles open (at *X* in the figure) the evaporation rose to a high level, nearly the same after sixteen weeks as after two.

By the mechanism now described, diffusion can only be regulated downwards.   Wigglesworth has discovered another mechanism by which the insect can meet increased demands and which is in its effects analogous to the opening up of capillaries in active muscles in vertebrates.

This mechanism is located in the non-chitinous tracheoles of less than 1 micron diameter which branch out from the smallest tracheæ and form a rich network[1] surrounding cells or penetrating into them, as in flight muscles where the tracheoles may even invest the single fibrils and sarcomeres. These final branches are normally invisible in the living insect, because they are filled with fluid, and the central point in

[1] It seems difficult to decide whether true networks exist or the final branches have free endings.   In several cases where loops have been described, e.g., in the tracheal gills of *Odonata* (fig. 83), a closer investigation has shown that each tracheole ends by itself.   From the point of view of oxygen supply the difference is irrelevant.

Wigglesworth's discovery is that this fluid moves back and forth
in relation to the call for oxygen of the tissue as illustrated in
the diagram (Fig. 68).   By the drawing back of the fluid in
the tracheoles, oxygen can reach the active cells by diffusion
through air instead of through fluid, and there is reason to
believe that the supply can exceed even that which is possible
by means of circulating blood in warm-blooded animals.   By
far the largest oxygen absorptions have been recorded for
flying insects.

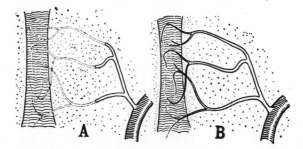

Fig. 68.   Tracheoles running to a muscle fibre; semischematic.   *A*, muscle
at rest; terminal parts of tracheoles contain fluid.   *B*, muscle fatigued; air
extends far into tracheoles.   (Wigglesworth.)

The mechanism of this regulation appears to be as follows:
The tracheole walls are permeable for water, and it should be
borne in mind that a high degree of permeability for oxygen
is, as far as we know, not physically possible without permeability for water.   The force of capillarity in tubes of the dimensions of tracheoles is very large, being about 10 atmospheres in a wet tube of 0.3μ diameter.   The osmotic pressure
of the tissue fluid is of the same order, and if we assume the
tracheoles to be "semi-permeable," that is, permeable to water
only, equilibrium should be attained with the meniscus at some
point in the tracheoles, while water should be unable to enter
the wider tracheæ.   Activity brings about an increase in the
osmotic concentration in the active tissue, and this should
cause the water to recede towards the narrower part of the
tracheole.   In a number of most beautiful experiments

Wigglesworth (1929, 1930, 1931) has shown that any increase in osmotic concentration has the effect anticipated.

Fig. 69 shows the effect of hypertonic potassium lactate on the air filling of tracheoles in an *Aeschna* larva.

In the firefly (*Photuris pennsylvanicus*) and in the European *Lampyridæ* the tracheal system of the segments bearing the light organs is independent of that of the rest of the body, and their

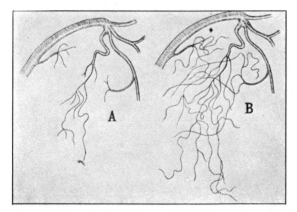

FIG. 69.   *A*, tracheal endings in mid-gut of *Aeschna* larva just after dissection,
B, after application of 3% potassium lactate.   (Wigglesworth.)

spiracles are kept closed during the daytime.   The flashes of light are initiated from the central nervous system, and Maluf (Maleouf, 1938) has brought forward good evidence to show that the mechanism is a sudden increase in osmotic pressure in the light-producing cells, causing the absorption of tracheolar fluid and an increased access of oxygen.   Maluf finds that injection of hypertonic substances produces a continuous glow.

A different conception of the mechanism regulating the movement of tracheolar fluid was put forward quite recently by T. Bult (1939) and supported by many experiments all made on the same object, the isolated mid-gut of the cockroach *Phyllodromia germanica*.   According to Bult, the tracheole walls are incompletely wetted by water and the effect of capillarity therefore quite low.   Evidence is presented to show that the movements are caused by swelling of proteins within cells, while the effect of osmotic changes in the hæmolymph are slight and secondary.

On the point which chiefly concerns us there is complete agreement with Wigglesworth: lack of oxygen is the main factor to cause retraction of fluid and an improved access of oxygen.

As the permeability of chitin for oxygen is quite low, there is reason to believe that oxygen is mainly absorbed through the walls of the tracheoles, while significant amounts of CO_2 can be eliminated all along the tracheæ and to some extent through the integument. One consequence of this is that lack of oxygen in any part of the tracheal system does not bring about any appreciable accumulation of CO_2 in the tracheæ involved.

Mechanical ventilation of the tracheal system combined with diffusion. In a number of insects of medium size or larger—as insects go—part of the tracheal system is ventilated by respiratory movements, but the gas transport in the narrower branches, often of several mm length, is always brought about by diffusion. The quantitative distinction between the part played by mechanical ventilation and diffusion respectively can be most conveniently illustrated by reference to an aquatic form, the larva of a large water beetle (*Dytiscus marginalis*). This animal has only one pair of functional spiracles on the last body segment. These are brought into contact with the surface, and a succession of rapid respirations takes place before the animal goes down again to seek its prey. The spiracles lead into two voluminous tracheæ running all the way up to the head and having an elliptic cross section. From these tracheæ a number of narrower tracheæ branch out to supply the organs, and all these are circular in cross section. Experiments were made (Krogh, 1920.3) to determine the volume of ordinary respirations (tidal air), of maximal respiration (vital capacity) and the internal volume of the tracheal system (total capacity). In the arrangement shown in Fig. 70 the depth of respiration can be read off directly by the movement of the meniscus in the

horizontal tube 2.   The expirations are seen to be active, and
the equilibrium position of the whole system is the inspiratory.
The normal depth of respiration which varied but little is
about 40 mm³ in an animal of 1 g weight.   The vital capacity

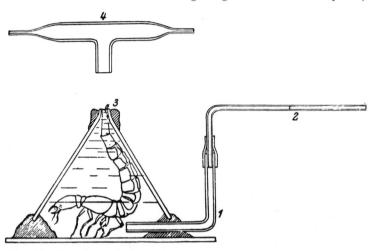

FIG. 70.   Experimental arrangement to study respiration in air-breathing
aquatic insects.   See text.   (Krogh.)

could be determined in different ways of which one was to
allow the animal to breathe pure oxygen from a slow current
of the gas through the tube 4 sealed on with plasticene to the
top of the funnel 3.   When the tracheæ were filled with oxygen
the normal stimulus for respiration would be much delayed,
the ventilation tracheæ would collapse completely, and when
the animal arrived at the surface some ineffectual attempts
would precede the sudden opening up.   The vital capacity
volume recorded by this was 60 mm³ and was confirmed also
by a different method.   The total capacity finally was determined by letting the animal breathe from a bubble of
known size and containing an indifferent gas which could be
determined by analysis.   From the dilution found after a
series of respirations the total capacity of the tracheal system
could be calculated and was found in the case considered to
be 90 mm³.   By a short series of normal respirations the air

making up the vital capacity or two-thirds of the total is evidently completely renewed, but in the remaining third part renewal can take place only by diffusion in the narrow, but numerous, circular tracheal branches.

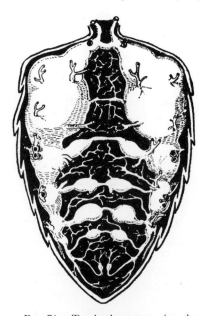

Fig. 71. Tracheal system in the abdomen of the honey-bee worker. Dorsal tracheae and air-sacs have been removed. (Snodgrass.)

The ventilation tracheæ in insects generally are either tubular with an elliptic cross section as in the example discussed above, or they have the form of air-sacs which can be of very varying form and shape from very numerous small vesicles (in the cockchafer) to very large structures like those shown in Fig. 71. In all cases, however, the final branches are circular in cross section and allow only diffusion transport. This is why even with mechanical ventilation of the air-sacs or tracheal trunks the size of insects must be limited by the amount of oxygen which can diffuse into their tissues. This limit was probably reached by the dragon-fly-like *Meganeura* of the Carbon period, which reached a length of over 30 cm, being 3 cm broad across the thorax.[1]

The ventilation usually takes place by movements of the abdomen either in the dorso-ventral direction or by telescoping the segments. In a few cases (*Dytiscus* and *Hydrophilus*, according to Brocher, 1931) there are respiratory movements

[1] Certain large air-sacs have very little to do with respiration, but have as their main function to take up space which in the rigid body of the insect may later be required for other purposes. This is the case with the two large proximal air-sacs in the abdomen of flies according to Evans (1935) and Fraenkel (1935). Their rôle is well illustrated by Fig. 72 after Evans.

also of thoracic segments.   As far as I know expiration is
always active, while the resting position brought about by the
elasticity of the integuments
and tracheal walls is normally the inspiratory.   Respiratory pauses in the
position of rest are not infre-
quent.   The respiratory
movements affect also the
air sacs at a distance by the
transfer of blood, and in this
way even some ventilation
of the legs can be brought
about.   Brocher (1920) describes the tracheal arrangement in the legs of the but-

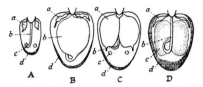

FIG. 72.   Diagram showing the part
played by the large air-sacs in the
abdomen of *Lucilia* during the growth
changes in the adult fly.   *A*, fly just
emerged.   *B*, after 5 minutes; gut filled
with air, distending abdomen.   *C*, after
10 hours; gut collapsed, air-sacs dis-
tended.   *D*, fully fed for 6 days; air-sacs
collapsed again while ovaries and fat
body fill abdomen.   *a* air-sacs, *b* gut,
c ovaries, *d* fat body.   (Evans.)

terfly *Sphinx convolvuli*.   There are narrow air-sacs separating
the muscles of the femur and separating also a dorsal from a

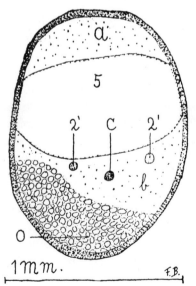

FIG. 73.   Cross section of tibia of
Sphinx.   *a* and *b*, blood lacunae; *5*, air
space.   (Brocher.)

ventral lacuna in which the
blood is flowing and the separation is continued right
down the leg, as illustrated
in Fig. 73.   In such a case
respiratory movements will
at the same time further the
blood flow and produce
some ventilation.

In experiments on grass-
hoppers, Krogh (1913) found
that the oxygen in the tibial
tracheæ was fairly high
(16%) when the animals
were quiet, but became reduced to 5% when they were
tired out by chasing them
about.   The ventilation,
which could amount to be-

tween 15 and 20% renewal at each breath, was evidently insufficient to sustain exertions for more than a couple of minutes, and this again illustrates the size limits imposed on insects.

In some large insects, especially among the *Orthoptera*, a unidirectional ventilation of the tracheal trunks has been noticed and in several cases closely studied (Du Buisson, 1924; Lee, 1925; McGovran, 1931; Fraenkel, 1932; Kitchel and Hoskins, 1935). It is brought about by opening and closing of spiracles in conformity with the rhythm of the respiratory movements. In most cases thoracic spiracles open during inspiration, and abdominal during expiration, producing an intermittent flow in the antero-posterior direction, but a reversal is occasionally observed (McArthur, 1929). Fraenkel made the most careful study of the relation between the respiratory movements and the opening and closing of spiracles, as illustrated in Fig.

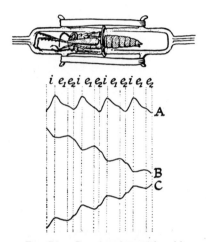

Fig. 74. Gas chamber with rubber partition enclosing grasshopper with thorax in anterior, abdomen in posterior compartment. *A* respiratory movements, *B* and *C* respectively fall in volume of thoracic compartment and increase in abdominal. *i* inspiratory phase, thoracic spiracles opened, abdominal closed; e_1 initial expiratory phase, all spiracles closed, e_2 final phase, abdominal spiracles opened. (Fraenkel.)

74, while Kitchel and Hoskins showed for the grasshopper *Chortophaga viridifasciata* that a pressure difference of over 20 cm water could be set up by the respiration of an animal mounted as in Fig. 74. The biological significance of the directed flow of air through a considerable part of the tracheal system lies in the fact that it reduces the dead space and therefore allows a better ventilation economy. This may be of great importance for the ventilation during flight.

Respiration during flight. Flight requires an enormous expenditure of energy which has to be provided by oxidation of food. This was first shown by Marie Parhon (1909) who measured the metabolism of a number of bees buzzing about in a large bottle. The figure arrived at, 20 litres of oxygen consumed per kg/h, was considered by many to be impossibly high, but it has been verified and even exceeded in later investigations. Kosmin et al. (1932) and finally Jongbloed and Wiersma (1935) in flight experiments on single bees of 5–6 minutes' duration observed values of 90 l/kg/h, or for the single bee, weighing 100 mg, 15 times its own volume per minute. Kalmus (1929) succeeded in inducing long-continued *stationary* flight in a butterfly, *Deilephila elpenor*, weighing about 600 mg, and found CO_2 productions of only 6.3 l/kg/h,[1] but Anne Raffy and P. Portier (1931) again obtained much higher figures on different butterflies by nicotine poisoning which simulates flight, and in quite recent unpublished experiments Zeuthen in this laboratory found on *Vanessa* (*atalanta* and *Io*) during actual flight values of 90 l/kg/h. The results represent increases over the resting metabolism of the insects studied of 50 to 200 times.

The enormous metabolic rate causes a considerable increase in the temperature of a flying insect, and it is a very characteristic fact, first observed by Dotterweich (1928), that many insects cannot fly until their temperature has been raised to a certain point, usually above 30°C. Dotterweich observed that several species of butterflies would vibrate their wings rapidly before flight and thereby raise the body temperature, in these cases to 36°C, before flight could begin.

It is a well-known fact that in the beetles belonging to the *Lamellicornia* flight is preceded by a series of deep "pumping" respirations, which were formerly thought to fill up the body with air. Recent experimentation (Krogh and Zeuthen, 1940) has shown that in this preparatory period body temperature is raised by static muscular contractions (demonstrated by

[1] The results appear *doubtful, because the metabolism found during rest, 168 ml/kg/hour, is much too low.

electromyograms) to about 32°, and that regular flight is not possible until this temperature is reached. The violent "pumping" ventilation provides the oxygen for this heat production.

During the flight itself an even larger ventilation must be necessary, but the mechanism of this ventilation differs greatly from one insect to another. Very instructive observations and experiments were made by Fraenkel (1932), who provoked flight movements reflexly in insects suitably fixed for observation.

In Wasps (*Vespa orientalis*) there is an increase of 5 to 10 times in amplitude of the abdominal respiratory movements, while the rhythm remains the same, but complete suppression of the abdominal ventilation does not prevent the flight of the wasp.

In the large grasshopper *Chistocerca gregaria* the abdominal ventilation often ceases completely for a couple of seconds when flight begins, but starts again with a much increased rhythm and slightly increased amplitude.

In *Libellula* the respiration goes on as during rest, but in the large butterflies (*Sphinx*, *Deilephila*), which practically do not ventilate during rest, respiratory movements with a rhythm of 30–40 become visible during flight.

In the cockchafer, which shows a greatly increased ventilation as a preparation for flight, this stops completely the moment actual flight begins. During a prolonged flight abdominal ventilation may start again after 2 to 3 minutes.

It is evident that the visible ventilation during flight cannot in any of the species studied be adequate to deal with the enormous increases in metabolism. The conclusion appears inevitable that the flight movements must themselves bring about the necessary ventilation of the flight muscles. Brocher (1920) has given a description of these muscles in the butterfly *Sphinx convolvuli* from which it appears that their rhythmic activity might act upon the air sacs surrounding the muscle bundles and perhaps upon the small tracheæ penetrating them so as to produce the necessary ventilation, but a more detailed study extended to several species among the good fliers is highly desirable.   Portier (1933) ascribes to the wings themselves in butterflies an important rôle in ventilation, but it appears more likely that his experimental results are due to interference with the circulation, which is of course of the utmost importance in muscles working at the rate of metabolism indicated above, even when it is not responsible for the oxygen supply.

The regulation of tracheal ventilation.   The ventilation of tracheæ in insects is, like the ventilation of the lungs in higher vertebrates, subject to a number of reflex influences, and it is not at present possible to make out the relative importance of chemical regulation and of reflex regulation, the more so as a quantitative formulation of the problem has not so far been attempted.

J. Stahn (1929) counted the respiration rhythm in *Dixippus* under the influence of varied atmospheres and found that even low concentrations of CO_2, from 0.2%, definitely increased the frequency.   It is known for a number of ventilating insects (Krogh, 1913; Hazelhoff, 1926, and others) that they react by increased ventilation to CO_2 in the inspired air.

Hazelhoff noted that while the spiracle reaction to CO_2 in the cockroach was instantaneous, the ventilation reaction took a couple of minutes to develop and remained for several minutes after the readmission of pure air, and this points definitely to a chemical mechanism acting on the nerve centers.

McGovran, who accurately measured the ventilation on grasshoppers (*Chortophaga, Dissosteira,* and *Arphia*), found increases up to 20 times the normal in 15% CO_2, but failed to detect any in 1%.

The regular opening and closing of spiracles which causes the ventilation to take place in a definite direction must necessarily be governed from the central nervous system and coupled with the ventilating movements.

In some of the insects (*Vespa, Macroglossum*) in which the visible respirations are increased during flight, Fraenkel found

that this increase is instantaneous and that the resting frequency and depth is restored immediately when the flight
stops, and concluded, no doubt rightly, that no chemical but
a purely reflex mechanism must be involved.

Adaptation of tracheal respiration to an aquatic existence. Among
the higher vertebrates respiring by lungs we found a small
number of forms which had secondarily taken to the water and
developed the necessary adaptations, all of them practically
along the same line, returning to the surface at intervals to
breathe. Among the tracheates a fairly large number have
become aquatic, but, partly owing to their small size, they
have been able to solve the respiratory problems in the most
diverse ways. In one point, however, they have proved in-
ferior to the aquatic vertebrates, they have not been able to
invade the oceans, and only very few can exist in brackish
water.

Respiration at the surface by diffusion. In the simplest type of
adaptation—from a physiological point of view—air-breathing
through spiracles is retained. The functional spiracles are

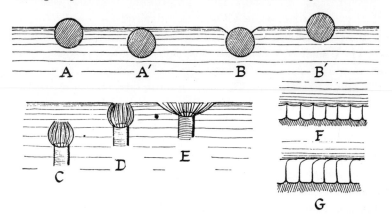

Fig. 75. *A*, hydrophile hair in the water surface, seen in cross-section.
A', position of equilibrium; *B*, hydrophobe hair in surface; *B'*, equilibrium; *C*,
spiracle surrounded by hydrophobe hairs (*Stratiomys*), position of equilibrium
below surface; *D*, reaching surface; *E*, in equilibrium; *F*, short hydrophobe hairs
on ventral cuticle of Dytiscus; *G*, curved hydrophobe hairs in *Elmis* and *Harmonia*.
(Wigglesworth.)

placed at one end of the body which is brought in contact with the surface, and in most cases the surface film is utilized for support by hydrofuge hairs or other structures (Fig. 75). It is essential that the spiracle opening itself is hydrophobe, so that water cannot possibly penetrate into the tracheal system.

In many small forms, of which the common mosquito larvæ (*Culex*) can be taken as typical, there is no mechanical ventilation, but the air in the system is renewed by diffusion only. This was shown in unpublished experiments by the writer as illustrated in Fig. 76. The larva is enclosed in the funnel of a micro gas-analysis tube, a small air-bubble is driven down so far that the spiracles can come in contact with it and focused upon by a horizontal microscope. When the larva comes in contact with the bubble after being submerged for several minutes a sudden upward jump of the meniscus is observed corresponding to a volume of 0.2–0.25 mm^3, but thereafter it does not indicate any respiratory movement whatever. During the period of submergence most of the oxygen in the tracheal system is used up and only to a slight extent replaced by CO_2, and the initial "inspiration" is simply the filling up of the partial vacuum created. The total volume of the tracheal system is about 1.5 mm^3, and the oxygen in it will suffice for the normal metabolism in 5–10 minutes.

As in the terrestrial insects, the diffusion type of ventilation imposes a size limit

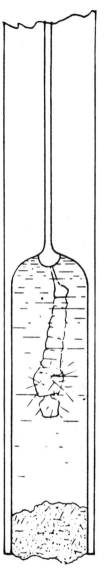

Fig. 76. Experimental arrangement to study ventilation in mosquito larva. (Krogh.)

which is narrowed in this case by the diffusion distance being the whole length of the body.

This type of respiration is supposed to exist in many mosquito larvæ. Generally the main tracheal trunks serve also as a reservoir for air, allowing the animal a dive of a number of minutes.

Mechanical ventilation at the surface. In many larger insects returning at intervals to the surface to breathe, the main tracheal trunks or a system of air sacs are ventilated mechanically, as described above for the larvæ of the large *Dytiscidæ*. In this group we find also the larvæ of the *Hydrophilinæ* and of several *Diptera*, especially the *Syrphidæ* (*Eristalis*) and *Stratiomyidæ*. The imagines of the larger *Dytiscidæ* and *Hydrophilinæ* and all stages of the genera *Nepa* and *Ranatra* also utilize this type of mechanism. Many of the imagines carry a supply of air also outside the tracheal system between the wings and the abdomen (*Dytiscus, Hydrophilus, Nepa*), and in the case of *Hydrophilus* also on the underside of the thorax where it is held by hydrofuge hairs. A quantitative study of the ventilation in many of these forms could be carried out without much experimental difficulty and could scarcely fail to give interesting results both œcologically and with regard to the regulation mechanisms.

In the large larvæ of *Stratiomyia*, Kuster (1933) describes a contractile "air chamber," outside the deeply sunk posterior spiracles which appears, according to his description, to have taken over the ventilation of the tracheal system proper, a most unusual arrangement which from the relative dimensions of the parts could scarcely be effective.

In *Eristalis*, Alsterberg (1934) describes a set of retractile rectal "gills" to which he ascribes the function of eliminating CO_2 directly to the water. This may be so, but seems rather unlikely in view of the powerful and generally continuous ventilation of the tracheal system.

Gill function of air stores. A number of insects carrying a store of air on the outside of the body supplement the oxygen brought down from the surface by diffusion of oxygen from the water, the air-water interface acting as a kind of gill. This conception was first put forward by Comstock (1887), who noticed some curious reactions in *Notonecta* which in badly aërated water apparently attempted to increase the surface of its air supply, but it was worked out quantitatively by Ege (1915) who also defined the conditions and limitations.

When an insect carrying a sheet of air on the outside stays under water for some time, a difference in oxygen tension between the water and the air carried down will be set up by the metabolic processes, and consequently oxygen will diffuse in from the water.   At a certain tension difference the rate of oxygen uptake may be sufficient to cover the metabolic requirements of the animal, but Ege showed that even in this case the air will have to be renewed from time to time at the surface.   This is due to the tension difference set up for nitrogen which will cause the total quantity of air to decrease all the time.   The O_2 used up is replaced with CO_2, but this diffuses away so rapidly that the nitrogen percentage rises. Supposing that the composition at equilibrium is 5% O_2 and 1% CO_2 the nitrogen percentage will be 94%, corresponding at the surface to $94/100 \times 760$ mm $= 713$ mm and at a depth of 1/2 meter to an additional pressure which is $94/100 \times \dfrac{760}{20} = 36$ mm or 749 mm in all, while the tension of the nitrogen dissolved in the water is only $79/100 \times 760 = 633$ mm.   Ege made a number of micro-analytic determinations of the actual composition of the air on *Corixa*, *Notonecta*, and some of the *Dytiscidæ* which fully bear out his calculations. They show a rapid reduction of the O_2 content with only a slight increase in the CO_2.   The experiments made show that a *Corixa* normally gets so much oxygen out of the water by diffusion into its air-covering that the supply will last 10 to 30 times as long as would otherwise be the case.   One experiment is specially instructive.   A *Notonecta* was put in water saturated with oxygen and allowed to breathe also from an atmosphere of pure oxygen.   In this case no perceptible diffusion could take place, and the animal became heavier than water in 14 minutes and died in 35 minutes, although when breathing ordinary air at the same temperature it could subsist for 6 hours without access to the surface.

This respiration mechanism is essential for several small aquatic insects belonging to different groups and also for some larger ones in winter when the metabolism is low.   Several species of *Dytiscidæ* move about vigorously under ice and supplement their store of air by catching bubbles rising from plants, or from the mud.   Even if these latter contain very little oxygen they may be essential for keeping up the quantity of gas on which the uptake of oxygen from the water depends.

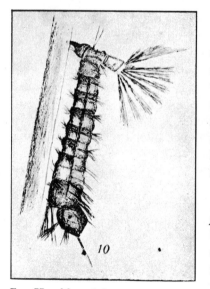

The animal which is probably most definitely adapted to obtain oxygen by diffusion into a layer of air is the spider *Argyroneta* which always carries a layer of air round the whole of the abdomen and part of the thorax. In this case the air sometimes lasts for several days even in summer (Braun, 1931).

Respiration from aquatic plants. A small number of beetle and *Diptera* larvæ are able to obtain air for their respiration from aquatic plants, not only by collecting bubbles, but directly from the intercellular spaces.

Fig. 77.   *Mansonia* larva on plant root. Ca. 10/1.   (Wesenberg-Lund.)

I have had an opportunity to make some observations and experiments on the larva of the mosquito *Mansonia* shown in Figs. 77 and 78.   The atrium of the spiracle is drawn out into a tube of hard chitin with a sharp cutting edge.   This is placed against the root or rhizoma of an aquatic plant and, by working the tail as a screw, is driven into the tissue until connection is established with the intercellular air spaces. The structure of the tracheal system showing an oval cross section of the main trunks and two air sacs would seem to invite mechanical ventilation, but the experiments failed to show anything but diffusion. In one of the experiments a larva was enclosed in a piece of glass tubing as shown in Fig. 79 with a root from an aquatic plant, mounted so that any desired gas mixture could be blown through the intercellular spaces. The larva very soon found and pierced the root, and the tracheal system could now conveniently be observed through a microscope. No respiratory movements took place while atmospheric air was passed through the root.

The oxygen percentage in the submerged roots is normally below 10% and may fall to 4%, and in winter even lower (Ege, 1915), and one might expect that low percentages were necessary to induce ventilation. Accordingly a gas mixture containing only 3.4% O_2 was passed

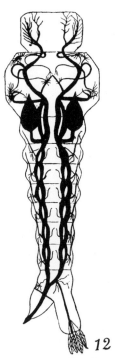

Fig. 78. Tracheal system of *Mansonia* larva. (Wesenberg-Lund.)

through. This did not impair the animal's vitality and did not induce any ventilation. Pure nitrogen paralyzed the animal, but likewise failed to induce respiratory movements.

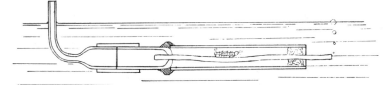

Fig. 79. Experimental arrangement to study ventilation in *Mansonia* larva. (Krogh.)

In special experiments it was shown that the compressibility
of the tracheal system, including the air sacs, is so slight that
an efficient ventilation is not within the power of the animal,
and the air sacs can function, in so far as they have any
respiratory significance, only as an oxygen store.

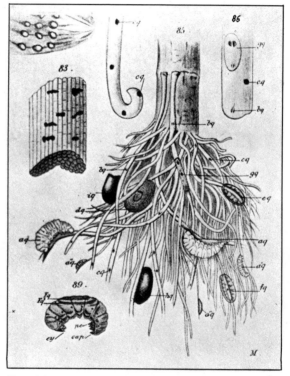

FIG. 80. *Donacia* larvæ and pupæ on *Ranunculus* roots (see text). About natural
size. (Böving.)

While the respiratory mechanism of the *Mansonia* larva appears simple and reasonably clear, the same cannot be said of
the *Donacia* larvæ. These animals, shown in Fig. 80 on the
roots of Ranunculus from which they feed, possess in connection with each of the last abdominal spiracles a slightly bent
very sharp chitin thorn (89 cy) which is inserted into the root
(86 bq).

Bøving (1906), who studied the morphology of the larvæ very carefully, is of opinion that these thorns are completely closed and that air must diffuse into them through a very thin chitinous membrane.   The metabolism, determined by Ege (1915) as 100 ml/kg/hour in a larva weighing 45 mg, is however much too high to allow this, and it is safe to assume that air penetrates from the plant through very narrow slits in the chitin.   In view of the often very low O_2 percentage in the plant roots and the size of the animal, it seems doubtful whether diffusion alone can be sufficient.   The larvæ have a number of spiracles (shown in Fig. 80), each provided with elaborate closing mechanisms.   These spiracles open to the water and allow air to pass out, as seen when a larva is put into hot water (Bøving).   They can serve only for mechanical expiration, and it is assumed both by Bøving and by Ege that active inspirations take place from the plant roots and expirations to the water, but it is a serious difficulty that the tracheal system shows, according to Bøving, no air sacs and tracheae only with a circular cross section.   No respiratory movements have been observed in nature.

Spiracles adapted to insertion in the roots of aquatic plants have been found recently in several other insect larvæ. Varley (1937) describes the arrangement in the syrphid fly *Chrysogaster*, in the ephydrid flies *Hydrellia* and *Notiphila*, and in the curculionid beetle *Linorhaptrus*.   Perhaps one of these might be better suited for experiments than *Donacia*.   Several genera of mosquitoes beside *Mansonia* also utilize the air in aquatic roots.   The peculiar structures must have been independently developed in the several families, and Varley mentions the case of the mosquito *Aediomyia* which may represent a possible developmental stage, putting the siphons, which show no special modifications, into gas bubbles and attempting to stick them into plants.

Tracheal gills.   A considerable number of aquatic insect larvæ have become completely independent of direct access to the air by the development of tracheal gills, characterized by a very dense system of fine tracheæ arranged just below the cuticle. When a difference is established between the oxygen pressure in these tracheæ and the tension in the surrounding water, oxygen will diffuse in from the water and become distributed by diffusion within the tracheal system to all parts of the body.

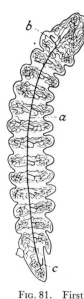

FIG. 81. First stage larva of *Macrocentrus gifuensis. Ichneumonidæ;* lateral view, to show the rich tracheal supply beneath the skin. (Parker.)

Considered simply as gills, the tracheal gills of insect larvæ duplicate practically all the gill arrangements observed in combination with a circulation, except those of fishes. We find cases like the one shown in Fig. 81 in which there is no branchial enlargement, but only a system of tracheæ below the cuticle. We find many cases of feathery or leaf-like tracheal gills differently arranged (*Plecoptera, Ephemeridæ, Trichoptera, Zygoptera, Gyrinidæ,* and others).

In some of these the gills are immobile and the renewal of water takes place by the locomotion of the animal. In others the gills themselves can be moved. In the *Trichoptera* larvæ inhabiting tubes we find the tube ventilated by suitable movements of the larvæ just as are the tubes of many *Annelida.*

We find finally in the nymphs of the large dragon flies (*Anisoptera*) a system of tracheal gills in the rectum presenting a very large surface (Fig. 82) and very richly supplied with tracheæ (Fig. 83). On *Aeschna* nymphs Koch (1936) measured the gill area and found it to be 7 cm² corresponding to an external surface of 3 cm². The gill system in these forms is curiously analogous to the gills of the cuttle fish (p. 38) and likewise ventilated by powerful muscular movements which may serve simultaneously for the locomotion of the animal and thus provide a close connection between the call for oxygen as determined by activity and the supply of oxygen to the gills.

The working of tracheal gill mechanisms is subject to certain physical conditions which have been clearly recognized and ably discussed by H. Koch (1936).

FIG. 82.   Dissection of rectum of *Libellula depressa* showing 6 double rows of tracheal gills.   Ca. 8/1.   (Koch.)

Just as in the air-gills described above, the nitrogen *percentage* in the enclosed air will practically always be higher than in the atmosphere, and the nitrogen would have the same

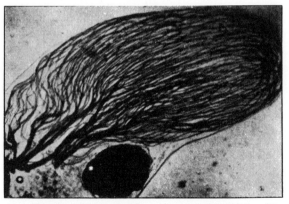

FIG. 83.   One branchial leaf with tracheoles.   Ca: 200/1.   (Koch.)

tendency to diffuse away and cause the ultimate disappearance of the whole of the air in the system, except for the fact that the walls of tracheal gills are rigid enough to stand a difference in total pressure which will allow the partial nitrogen pressure in the system to be in equilibrium with the tension of dissolved nitrogen in the surrounding water.   There is, and must be normally,[1] a permanent relative vacuum in a tracheal system supplied by gills.   By a number of very ingenious experiments and analyses Koch demonstrated the rigidity of the tracheal walls in *Aeschna* nymphs and measured the total pressure of the enclosed gases, which he found to be about 90% of the atmospheric and practically independent of the depth at which the animals were living.

The indispensable rigidity of the whole tracheal system precludes the existence of any mechanical ventilating arrangements and leaves only diffusion as the mechanism for distributing the oxygen absorbed through the tracheal gills. Calculations, based on measurements of the tracheal trunks, and analyses made by Krogh (1920) show that an oxygen pressure difference of about 40 mm will be required to transport the necessary oxygen to the thorax and head from the gills in the rectum.   This makes it easy to understand that, in spite of the high perfection of the tracheal gill system, the dragon fly nymphs begin to suffer from oxygen lack when the tension in the water sinks below 55 mm.   It is clear also that the large species of dragon flies come close to the size limit attainable with this type of tracheal system.

In many cases tracheal gills are sufficiently rigid to allow the necessary uptake of oxygen from moist air, but in dry air they lose too much water.   It is interesting that in some in-

[1] When the water becomes supersaturated to any considerable extent the pressure in the closed tracheal system will rise above the atmospheric, and several forms breathing through tracheal gills are provided with safety valves in the form of spiracles allowing any excess pressure to blow off into the water. Koch (1934) has utilized this in a most ingenious way to measure the relative importance of the caudal lamellæ in *Agrion pulchellum* nymphs.   Placing such a nymph in water, presenting a slight supersaturation of CO_2, and opening the tracheal system, he measured the interval in seconds between bubbles being released, before and after removing the caudal lamellæ.   In one case the average interval in the intact larva was 64 seconds, while after removal of the three lamellæ it rose to 115 seconds, indicating that in this case 45% of the total respiration could take place through the caudal lamellæ.

By a judicious application of this method several disputed problems concerning the respiration through tracheal gills proper and the general surface could no doubt be solved.

sects, of which the pupal stage of the mosquito *Simulium subornatum* is a good example, a respiratory gill mechanism has been evolved which can be used both in dry air and in water (Nadine Pulikovsky, 1927). The pupæ are fixed to stones in mountain streams which dry up often enough. Outside the spiracles we find the hollow air-filled cuticular appendage shown in Fig. 84 into which oxygen can diffuse with equal facility from air and from water.

FIG. 84. *Simulium subornatum* pupa with cuticular appendages. Ca. 7/1. (Pulikovsky.)

The regulation of respiration in aquatic insects has not been studied in any exhaustive or comprehensive way. In several of the insects carrying a supply of air down with them, the decrease in buoyancy appears to be the normal stimulus for returning to the surface (*Corixa, Notonecta*), but lack of oxygen will no doubt turn out to be effective in almost all cases and has been shown to regulate the movements by which *Phryganea* larvæ ventilate their tubes (van Dam, 1938), the rhythmic vibrations of the gills in ephemerid larvæ and the ventilation of the gills in Odonata. In these cases the supply of oxygen-saturated water produces a long continued apnœa (Babák and Foustka, 1907).

Botjes (1932) made experiments to show that the movements of the hind legs of *Corixa*, which apparently serve to renew the water along the air store in the abdomen, are initiated by high CO_2 tensions. The observation that such movements are induced by CO_2 tensions of 40–45 mm (6%) is no doubt correct, but such high tensions must be rare in the natural habitat of *Corixa*, and no attempt has been made to show that they are ever met with. On the other hand Botjes was unable to induce the movements by oxygen lack which will bring the animal to the surface. This problem, like so many others concerning the respiratory mechanisms in the animal kingdom, will have to be studied again by improved methods.

IX

CONCLUDING REMARKS

THE literature concerning respiratory mechanisms from morphological, physiological, and œcological points of view is very large, and no attempt has been made in the preceding pages to cover it, but rather to give representative examples of the ways in which the problems of respiration and especially of the oxygen supply have been solved in the animal kingdom, and to arrange these examples into a kind of physiological system, built up on analogy of function. It has been attempted to show how the solutions reached are governed by physical and chemical conditions and how quantitative formulations of ideas and theories are necessary to bring out the salient features.

It is hoped also that this presentation may serve as a stimulus to further studies, and it may be appropriate to indicate certain lines along which research is desirable and will probably be fruitful.

One such line is the study of ventilation regulation as influenced by varied concentrations of oxygen and CO_2. It is essential in such studies that the animal be held or confined without being cramped or disturbed—in many cases a light narcosis may be very useful—and it is necessary not only to count or record respiratory movements, but to obtain quantitative measurements of the ventilation. In many studies, even quite recent ones, the mistake has been made of using CO_2 concentrations much higher than those which can be encountered in nature, with the result that the regulating effects have been missed entirely and only the narcotic effect observed.

An important but difficult line of attack is to study metabolism and respiratory mechanisms under stress. In some cases exposure to low oxygen concentration will be adequate as a source of stress, but the most interesting results are to be expected from an investigation of locomotor activity. It is no doubt technically possible to study metabolism and respiration of fishes during swimming at a constant rate, and of certain insects and birds during flight, and to obtain information similar to that obtained on man during work on a bicycle ergometer or a treadmill. A combination of activity with reduced oxygen pressure may give valuable clues. Experiments along this line have been planned by the writer.

Finally I should like to draw attention to the problems connected with prolonged oxygen lack. It is scarcely possible to state anything definite from the material available, but from the observations on many different animals, from worms and insects to diving mammals, the impression remains that the continued provision of quite small and in themselves absolutely insufficient amounts of oxygen is essential for the successful resistance against asphyxiation. The mechanism may differ from one case to another. In the higher forms it may be the central nervous system which is protected against (physiological) disintegration by a small amount of oxygen, but it may be a more fundamental phenomenon, perhaps analogous to the necessity of metabolizing a little carbohydrate along with fats.

LIST OF REFERENCES

Abolin, L. (1924.) Einfluss der maximalen Darmatmung auf den histologischen Bau des Enddarmes des Schlammpeizgers. Biol. Zbl. **44**, 433–458.

Agar, W. E. (1908.) On the appearance of vascular filaments on the pectoral fin of Lepidosiren paradoxa. Anat. Anz. **33**, 27–30.

Alsterberg, G. (1922.) Die respiratorischen Mechanismen der Tubificiden. Eine experimentell-physiologische Untersuchung auf oekologischer Grundlage. Lunds Univ. Aarsskr. N. F. Avd. 2. **18**, 1–176.

Alsterberg, G. (1934.) Beiträge zur Kenntnis der Anatomie und Biologie der limnophilen Syrphidenlarven. Biol. Zbl. **54**, 1–20.

Babák, E. (1907.) Ueber die funktionelle Anpassung der äusseren Kiemen beim Sauerstoffmangel. Zbl. Physiol. **21**, 97–99.

Babák, E. (1912.) Die Mechanik und Innervation der Atmung. Wintersteins Handb. vergl. Physiol. **1**, 265–918.

Babák, E., u. O. Foustka. (1907.) Untersuchungen über den Auslösungsreiz der Atembewegungen bei den Libelluliden-larven (und Arthropoden überhaupt). Pfl. Arch. **119**, 530–548.

Backman, E. L. (1915.) Om syrgasens tension i kroppsvätskan hos Coelenterater i fritt tillstånd i hafvet och efter vistelse i akvarium. Upsala Läkaref. Förh. **20**, 287–302.

Baer, M. (1896.) Beiträge zur Kenntnis der Anatomie und Physiologie der Athemwerkzeuge bei den Vögeln. Z. wiss. Zool. **61**, 420–498.

Baglioni, S. (1910.) Zur vergleichenden Physiologie der Atembewegungen der Wirbeltiere. I. Fische. Ergebn. Physiol. **9**, 90–137.

Barcroft, J. (1922.) The raison d'être of the red corpuscle. Harvey Lect. **17**, 146–161.

Barcroft, J. (1928.) The respiratory function of the blood. Part II. Hæmoglobin. Cambridge. 1–200.

Barcroft, J. (1934.) Features in the architecture of physiological function. Macmillan Co., New York.

Barcroft, J., and H. Barcroft. (1924.) The blood pigment of Arenicola. Proc. Roy. Soc. B, **96**, 28–42.

Barcroft, J., R. H. E. Elliott, L. B. Flexner, F. G. Hall, W. Herkel, E. F. McCarthy, T. McClurkin, and M. Talaat. (1934.) Conditions of foetal respiration in the goat. J. Physiol. **83**, 192–214.

Bare, C. O. (1928.) Hæmoglobin cells and other studies of the genus Buenoa (Hemiptera, Notonectidæ). Univ. Kansas, Science Bull. **18**, 265–317.

Begemann, H. (1924.) Over de ademhalingsfunctie van haemocyanine. Proefschrift. Utrecht.

Bepler, H. (1909.) Ueber die Atmung der Oniscoideen. Diss. Greifswald.

Berg, K. (1938.) Studies on the bottom animals of Esrom Lake. Mem. Acad. Roy. Sc. Lett. Danemark. **8**, 1–255.

Bernard, H. M. (1895.) The comparative morphology of the Galeodidæ. Trans. Linn. Soc. II, **6**, Zool. 305–417.

Bertolini, F. (1933.) Sulle funzioni dei polmoni acquatici delle Oloturie. Pubbl. Staz. zool. Napoli, **13**, 1–11.

Bertolini, F. (1935.) Ricerche sugli organi respiratori delle Oloturie. Atti R. Ist. veneto. **94**, 9–11.

Bevelander, G. (1931.) The gills of Amia calva specialized for respiration in an oxygen deficient habitat. Copeia, **1931**, 123–127.

Black, E. C., and L. Irving. (1937.) The effect of carbon dioxide upon the oxygen capacity of the blood of the carp (Cyprinus carpio L.). Trans. Roy. Soc. Canada, Biol. Sc. **31**, 29–32.

Bohr, Chr. (1897.) Bidrag til Svømmefuglenes Fysiologi. K. Danske Vid. Selsk. Forh. **1897**, 207–234.

Bohr, Chr., K. Hasselbalch, u. A. Krogh. (1904.) Ueber einen in biologischer Beziehung wichtigen Einfluss, den die Kohlensäurespannung des Blutes auf dessen Sauerstoffbindung übt. Skand. Arch. Physiol. **16**, 402–412.

Bøje, O. (1933.) Ueber die Grösse der Lungen-diffusion des Menschen während Ruhe und körperlicher Arbeit. Arbeitsphysiol. **7**, 157–166.

Böker, H. (1933.) Ueber einige neue Organe bei luftatmenden Fischen (usw.). Anat. Anz. **76**, 148–154.

Borden, Mabel A. (1931.) A study of the respiration and of the function of hæmoglobin in Planorbis corneus and Arenicola marina. J. Mar. Biol. Ass. Plymouth, **17**, 709–738.

Bornebusch, C. H. (1930.) The fauna of forest soil. Diss. Copenhagen.

Botjes, O. (1932.) Die Atemregulierung bei Corixa geoffroyi Leach. Z. vergl. Physiol. **17**, 557–564.

Bøving, A. G. (1906.) Bidrag til Kundskaben om Donaciin-Larvernes Naturhistorie. Diss. København.

Brandes, G. (1924.) Beobachtungen und Reflexionen über die Atmung der Vögel. Pfl. Arch. **203**, 492–511.

Braun, F. (1931/32.) Beiträge zur Biologie und Atmungsphysiologie der Argyroneta aquatica. Zool. Jahrb. Abt. Syst. **62**, 175–262.

Brinkman, R. (1933.) The occurrence of carbonic anhydrase in lower marine animals. J. Physiol. **80**, 171–173.

Brocher, F. (1920.) Étude expérimentale sur le fonctionnement du vaisseau dorsal et sur la circulation du sang chez les Insectes. III. Le Sphinx convolvuli. Arch. de zool. exp. gén. **60**, 1–45.

Brocher, F. (1931.) Le mécanisme de la respiration et celui de la circulation du sang chez les insectes. Arch. Zool. exp. gén. **74**, 25–32.

Brody, S., and R. Cunningham. (1936.) Growth and development with special reference to domestic animals. XL. Comparison between efficiency of horse, man, and motor, with special reference to size and monetary economy. Res. Bull. Univ. Missouri, **244**, 5–56.

Buddenbrock, W. v. (1938.) Einige Beobachtungen über die Tätigkeit der Wasserlungen der Holothurien. Z. vergl. Physiol. **26**, 303–305

Buddenbrock, W. v., u. G. v. Rohr. (1923.) Die Atmung von Dixippus morosus. Z. f. allg. Physiol. **20**, 111–160.

Budgett, J. S. (1900.) Observations on Polypterus and Protopterus. Proc. Cambr. Philos. Soc. **10**, 236–240.

Buisson, M. du. (1924.) Observations sur le ventilation tracheenne des insectes. Bull. Acad. Roy. Belg. Cl. Sc. V, **10**, 373–391, 635–656.

Buisson, M. du. (1924.) Observations sur le mecanisme de la ventilation trachienne. II. Ibid., 635–656.

Buisson, M. du. (1925.) Récherches sur la circulation sanguine et la ventilation pulmonaire chez les Scorpions. Bull. Acad. Roy. Belg. Cl. Sc. V, 11, 666–680.

Bult, T. (1939.) Over de beweging der vloeistoff in de tracheolen der insecten. Proefschrift. Groningen.

Buxton, P. A. (1930.) Evaporation from the meal-worm (Tenebrio: Coleoptera) and atmospheric humidity. Proc. Roy. Soc. B, 106, 560–577.

Carter, G. S. (1931.) Aquatic and aerial respiration in animals. Biol. Rev. Cambridge philos. Soc. 6, 1–35.

Carter, G. S. (1935.) Respiratory adaptations of the fishes of the forest waters, with descriptions of the accessory respiratory organs of Electrophorus electricus (Linn.) and Plecostomus plecostomus (Linn.). J. Linn. Soc. Zool. 39, 219–233.

Carter, G. S., and L. C. Beadle. (1930.) Notes on the habits and development of Lepidosiren paradoxa. J. Linn. Soc. Zool. 37, 197–203.

Carter, G. S., and L. C. Beadle. (1930.) The fauna of the swamps of the Paraguayan Chaco in relation to its environment. II. Respiratory adaptations in the fishes. J. Linn. Soc. Zool. 37, 327–368.

Cheatum, E. P. (1934.) Limnological investigations on respiration, annual migratory cycle, and other related phenomena in fresh-water pulmonate snails. Trans. Amer. Micr. Soc. 53, 348–407.

Christensen, E. Hohwü. (1931.) Beiträge zur Physiologie schwerer körperlicher Arbeit. V. Mitt.: Minutenvolumen und Schlagvolumen des Herzens während schwerer körperlicher Arbeit. Arbeitsphysiol. 4, 470–502.

Christensen, E. Hohwü, and D. B. Dill. (1935.) Oxygen dissociation curves of bird blood. J. Biol. Chem. 109, 443–448.

Christiansen, Johanne, C. G. Douglas, and J. S. Haldane. (1914.) The absorption and dissociation of carbon dioxide by human blood. J. Physiol. 48, 244–271.

Comstock, J. H. (1887.) Note on respiration of aquatic bugs. Amer. Nat. 21, 577–578.

Cunningham, J. T. (1929.) The vascular filaments on the pelvic limbs of Lepidosiren, their function and evolutionary significance. Proc. Roy. Soc. B, 105, 484–493.

Cunningham, J. T., and D. M. Reid. (1932.) Experimental researches on the emission of oxygen by the pelvic filaments of the male Lepidosiren with some experiments on Symbranchus marmoratus. Proc. Roy. Soc. London B, **110**, 234–248.

Dahr, E. (1924.) Die Atembewegungen der Landpulmonaten. Lunds Univ. Aarsskr. N. F. Avd. 2, **20**, Nr. 10, 1–19.

Dahr, E. (1927.) Studien über die Respiration der Landpulmonaten. Lunds Univ. Aarsskr. N. F. Avd. 2, **23**, Nr. 10, 1–118.

Dam L. van. (1935.) On the utilization of oxygen by Mya arenaria. J. exp. Biol. **12**, 86–94.

Dam, L. van. (1938.) On the utilizaton of oxygen and regulation of breathing in some aquatic animals. Diss. Groningen.

Darwin, Ch. (1851.) A monograph on the sub-class Cirripedia. The Lepadidæ. London.

Darwin, Ch. (1854.) A monograph on the sub-class Cirripedia. The Balandiæ. London.

Das, B. K. (1928.) The bionomics of certain air-breathing fishes of India, together with an account of the development of their air-breathing organs. Phil. Trans. Roy. Soc. B, **216**, 183–219.

Das, B. K. (1934.) The habits and structure of Pseudapocryptes lanceolatus, a fish in the first stages of structural adaptation to aerial respiration. Proc. Roy. Soc. B, **115**, 422–430, 1934.

Dijk, P. J. S. van. (1938.) Ueber die Regelung der Labyrinthatmung bei jungen und erwachsenen Exemplaren von Osphromenus gurami. Z. vergl. Physiol. **26**, 328–346.

Dijkstra, S. J. (1933.) Ueber Wesen und Ursache der Notatmung. Z. vergl. Physiol. **19**, 666–672.

Dill, D. B. (1938.) Life, heat and altitude. Cambridge, Mass.

Dill, D. B., and H. T. Edwards. (1931.) Physicochemicalproperties of crocodile blood (Crocodilus acutus, Cuvier). J. Biol. Chem. **90**, 515–530.

Dill, D. B., H. T. Edwards, and M. Florkin. (1932.) Properties of the blood of the skate (Raia ocellata). Biol. Bull. **62**, 23–36.

Dolk, H. E., u. F. van der Paauw. (1929.) Die Leistungen des Hämoglobins beim Regenwurm. Z. vergl. Physiol. **10**, 324–343.

Dolk, H. E., u. N. Postma. (1927.) Ueber die Haut- und die Lungenatmung von Rana temporaria. Z. vergl. Physiol. **5**, 417–444.

Dotterweich, H. (1928.) Beiträge zur Nervenphysiologie der Insekten. I. Das Schwirren der Schmetterlinge vor dem Fluge. Zool. Jb. Abt. Allg. Zool. **44**, 399–450.

Drastich, L. (1925.) Ueber das Leben der Salamandra-Larven bei hohem und niedrigem Sauerstoffpartialdruck. Z. vergl. Physiol. **2**, 632–657.

Edwards, H. T. (1936.) Lactic acid in rest and work at high altitude. Am. J. Physiol. **116**, 367–375.

Ege, R. (1915.) On the respiratory conditions of the larva and pupa of Donaciae. Vid. Medd. Dansk Naturh. Forening, **66**, 183–196.

Ege, R. (1915.) On the respiratory function of the air stores carried by some aquatic insects (Corixidæ, Dytiscidæ, and Notonecta). Z. f. allg. Physiol. **17**, 81–124.

Ege, R. (1916.) Less known respiratory media (Danish). Vid. Medd. D. Naturh. Forening, **67**, 14–16.

Eggert, B. (1929.) Bestimmungstabelle und Beschreibung der Arten der Familie Periophthalmus. Z. wiss. Zool. **133**, 398–410.

Eisig, H. (1881.) Ueber das Vorkommen eines schwimmblasen-ähnlichen Organs bei Anneliden. Mitt. Zool. Stat. Neapel, **2**, 255–304.

Eisig, H. (1887.) Monographie der Capitelliden des Golfes von Neapel. Fauna u. Flora des Golfes von Neapel. XVI.

Erikson, H. (1940.) In preparation. Hvaalradets Skr. det. Norske Vid. Akad. Oslo, 1940.

Evans, A. C. (1935.) Some notes on the biology and physiology of the sheep blowfly, Lucilia sericata, Meig. Bull. Ent. Res. **26**, 115–122.

Faurholt, K. (1924.) Études sur les solutions aqueuses d'anhydride carbonique et d'acide carbonique. J. .Chim. Phys. **21**, 400–455.

Ferguson, J. K. W., L. Lewis, and J. Smith. (1937.) The distribution of carbonic anhydrase in certain marine invertebrates. J. cell. a. comp. Physiol. **10**, 395–400.

Fischer, G. (1905.) Vergleichend-anatomische Untersuchungen über den Bronchialbaum der Vögel. Zoologica, **19**, 1–45.

Florkin, M. (1933.) Recherches sur les hémérythrines. Arch. Int. Physiol. **36**, 247–328.

Florkin, M. (1934.) La fonction respiratoire du "milieu intérieur" dans la série animale. Ann. Physiol. **10**, 599–694.

Fox, D. L., H. U. Sverdrup, and J. P. Cunningham. (1937.) The rate of water propulsion by the California mussel. Biol. Bull. **72**, 417–438.

Fox, H. Munro. (1921.) Methods of studying the respiratory exchange in small aquatic organisms, with particular reference to the use of flagellates as an indicator for oxygen consumption. J. gen. Physiol. **3**, 565–573.

Fox, H. Munro. (1926.) Chlorocruorin: a pigment allied to hæmoglobin. Proc. Roy. Soc. Ser. B, **99**, 199–220.

Fox, H. Munro. (1932.) The oxygen affinity of chlorocruorin. Proc. Roy. Soc. B, **111**, 356–363.

Fox, H. Munro, and M. L. Johnson. (1934.) The control of respiratory movements in Crustacea by oxygen and carbon dioxide. J. exp. Biol. **11**, 1–10.

Fraenkel, G. (1930.) Der Atmungsmechanismus des Skorpions. Z. vergl. Physiol. **11**, 656–661.

Fraenkel, G. (1930.) Untersuchungen über die Atmung der Insekten. Vortrag vor dem Internat. Zool.-Kongress in Padua (im Druck).

Fraenkel, G. (1932.) Untersuchungen über die Koordination von Reflexen und automatisch-nervösen Rhytmen bei Insekten. II. Die nervöse Regulierung der Atmung während des Fluges. Z. vergl. Physiol. **16**, 394–417.

Fraenkel, G. (1932.) Untersuchungen über die Koordination von Reflexen und automatisch-nervösen Rhytmen bei Insekten. IV. Das Problem des gerichteten Atemstromes in den Tracheen der Insekten. Z. vergl. Physiol. **16**, 418–443.

Fraenkel, G. (1935.) Observations and experiments on the blowfly (Calliphora erythrocephala) during the first day after emergence. Proc. Zool. Soc. L. **1935**, 893–904.

Fraenkel, G., and G. V. B. Herford. (1938.) The respiration of insects through the skin. J. exp. Biol. **15**, 266–280.

Gage, S. H., and Susanna P. Gage. (1886.) Aquatic respiration in soft-shelled turtles: a contribution to the physiology of respiration in vertebrates. The Amer. Naturalist, **20**, 233–236.

Galtsoff, P. S. (1928.) The effect of temperature on the mechanical activity of the gills of the oyster (Ostrea virginica Gm.). J. gen. Physiol. **11**, 415–431.

Gerbig, F. (1913.) Ueber Tipuliden-Larven mit besonderer Berücksichtigung der Respirationsorgane. Zool. Jahrb. Abt. Syst. **35**, 127–184.

Goor, H. van. (1937.) La répartition de l'anhydrase carbonique dans l'organisme des animaux. Arch. int. Physiol. **45**, 491–509.

Gray, J. (1932.) The osmotic properties of the eggs of the trout (Salmo fario). J. exp. Biol. **9**, 277–299.

Graham, T. (1833.) On the law of the diffusion of gases. Phil. Mag. III, **2**, 354–356.

Green, Arda A., and R. W. Root. (1933.) The equilibrium between hemoglobin and oxygen in the blood of certain fishes. Biol. Bull. **64**, 383–404.

Gunn, D. L. (1933.) The temperature and humidity relations of the cockroach (Blatta orientalis). I. Desiccation. J. exp. Biol. **10**, 274–285.

Haase, E. (1885.) Das Respirationssystem der Symphylen und Chilopoden. Zool. Beitr. **1**, 65–96.

Haldane, J. S. (1922.) Respiration. New Haven.

Haldane, J. S., and J. G. Priestley. (1905.) The regulation of the lung-ventilation. J. Physiol. **32**, 225–266.

Haldane, R. C. (1907.) Report of the Admiralty Committee on Deep Water Diving. Parl. Paper, C. N., 1549.

Hall, F. G. (1930.) The ability of the common mackerel and certain other marine fishes to remove dissolved oxygen from sea water. Amer. J. Physiol. **93**, 417–421.

Hall, F. G. (1934.) Hæmoglobin function in the developing chick. J. Physiol. **83**, 222–228.

Hall, F. G., D. B. Dill, and E. S. G. Barron. (1936.) Comparative physiology in high altitudes. J. cell. a. comp. Physiol. **8**, 301–313.

Hall, V. E. (1931.) The muscular activity and oxygen consumption of Urechis caupo. Biol. Bull. **61**, 400–416.

Hansen, E. (1934.) Ueber die Sauerstoffschuld bei körperlicher Arbeit. Arbeitsphysiol. **8**, 151–171.

Hansen, H. J. (1893/94.) Organs and characters in different orders of Arachnida. Entomologiske Medd. **4**, 135–44.

Harnisch, O. (1935.) Versuch einer Analyse des Sauerstoffverbrauchs von Tubifex Tubifex Müll. Z. vergl. Physiol. **22**, 450–465.

Harnisch, O. (1936.) Primäre und sekundäre Oxybiose der Larve von Chironomus Thummi (nebst ergänzenden Messungen an Tubifex Tubifex). Z. vergl. Physiol. **23**, 391–419.

Harnisch, O. (1937.) Primäre und sekundäre Oxybiose wirbelloser Tiere. Verh. d. Dtsch. Zool. Ges. **1937**, 129–136.

Hartridge, H., and F. J. W. Roughton. (1927.) The rate of distribution of dissolved gases between the red blood corpuscle and its fluid environment. I. Preliminary experiments on the rate of uptake of oxygen and carbon monoxide by sheep's corpuscles. J. Physiol. **62**, 232–242.

Harvey, E. (1928.) The oxygen consumption of luminous bacteria. J. gen. Physiol. **11**, 469–475.

Hazelhoff, E. H. (1926.) Regeling der Ademhaling bij Insecten en Spinnen. Proefschrift. Utrecht.

Hazelhoff, E. H. (1938.) Ueber die Ausnutzung des Sauerstoffs bei verschiedenen Wassertieren. Z. vergl. Physiol. **26**, 306–327.

Heerdt, P. F. v., u. B. J. Krijgsman. (1939.) Die Regulierung der Atmung bei Eriocheir sinensis Milne Edwards. Z. vergl. Physiol. **27**, 29–40.

Henderson, L. J. (1928.) Blood. A study in general physiology. New Haven.

Henderson, Yandell. (1939.) The last thousand feet on Everest. Nature, **143**, 921–923.

Henriques, O. M. (1929.) Ueber Carbhämoglobin. Ergebn. Physiol. **28**, 1–65.

Henze, M. (1910.) Ueber den Einfluss des Sauerstoffdrucks auf den Gaswechsel einiger Meerestiere. Biochem. Z. **26**, 255–278.

Herford, G. M. (1938.) Tracheal pulsation in the flea. J. Exp. Biol. **15**, 327–338.

Hill, A. V. (1924.) Muscular activity. Herter Lectures. Baltimore.

Hill, A. V., C. N. H. Long, and H. Lupton. (1924.) Muscular exercise, lactic acid, and the supply and utilisation of oxygen. Parts IV–VI. Proc. Roy. Soc. B, **97**, 84–138.

Hurtado, A. (1937.) Aspectos fisiologicos y patologicos de la vida en la altura. Rev. med. peruana, **9**, 3–52.

Hurtado, A., A. Rotta, C. Merino, and J. Pons. (1937.) Studies of myohemoglobin at high altitudes. Amer. J. Med. Sc. **194**, 708–713.

Huxley, Th. (1882.) On the respiratory organs of Apteryx. Proc. Zool. Soc. 560–569.

Irving, L. (1935.) The diving habits of the beaver. Science, **82**, 569.

Irving, L. (1937.) The respiration of beaver. J. cell. a. comp. Physiol. **9**, 437–451.

Irving, L. (1938.) Changes in the blood flow through the brain and muscles during the arrest of breathing. Am. J. Physiol. **122**, 207–214.

Irving, L. (1938.) Control of respiration in diving animals. Am. J. Physiol. **123**, 107.

Irving, L. (1938.) The insensitivity of diving animals to CO_2. Am. J. Physiol. **124**, 729–734.

Irving, L. (1939.) Respiration in diving mammals. Physiol. Rev. **19**, 112–134.

Irving, L., O. M. Solandt, D. Y. Solandt, and K. C. Fisher. (1935.) The respiratory metabolism of the seal and its adjustment to diving. J. cell. a. comp. Physiol. **7**, 137–151.

Jongbloed, J., u. C. A. G. Wiersma. (1934.) Der Stoffwechsel der Honigbiene während des Fliegens. Z. vergl. Physiol. **21**, 519–533.

Jordan, H. J. (1922.) Ueber Tiere mit inkonstanter alveolärer Gasspannung (quotes measurements by Hazelhoff). Bijdragen tot de Dierkunde (Weber Festschrift).

Jordan, H. J. (1925.) Ueber die Rolle des Hämocyanins bei der Atmung. Kurze Mitteilung nach einer in niederländischer Sprache erschienenen Dissertation von Herman Begemann. Z. vergl. Physiol. **2**, 381–391.

Jordan, H. J. (ref. Hazelhoff). (1927.) Die Regulierung der Atmung bei Insekten und Spinnen. Z. vergl. Physiol. **5**, 179–190.

Jordan, H. J., u. J. Guittart. (1938.) Die Regulierung der Atmung bei Astacus fluviatilis. K. Nederl. Akad. v. Wetensch. Amsterdam, Proc. **41**, 3–10.

Juillet, A. (1911.) Rapports des sacs aériens et des bronches chez les oiseaux. C. R. Acad. Sc. **152**, 1024–1026.

Kalmus, H. (1929.) Die CO_2-Produktion beim Fluge von Deilephila elpenor (Weinschwärmer). Baustein zu einer Energetik des Tierfluges. z. vergl. Physiol. **10**, 445–455.

Kawamoto, N. (1927.) The anatomy of Caudina chilensis (J. Müller) with especial reference to the perivisceral cavity, the blood and the water vascular systems in their relation to the blood circulation. Sc. Rep. Tôhoku Univ. IV Biol. **2**, 239–264.

Kawamoto, N. (1928.) Oxygen capacity of the blood of certain invertebrates which contains hæmoglobin. Sc. Rep. Tôhoku Imp. Univ. IV Biol. **3**, 561–575.

Keilin, D. (1925.) On cytochrome, a respiratory pigment, common to animals, yeast, and higher plants. Proc. Roy. Soc. London, B. **98**, 312–339.

Kemnitz, G. A. v. (1917.) Untersuchungen über den Stoffbestand und Stoffwechsel der Larven von Gastrophilus equi (Clark), nebst Bemerkungen über den Stoffbestand der Larven von Chironomus (spec.?) L. Z. f. Biol. **67**, 129–244.

Keys, A. (1938.) Die Wirkung des Höhenklimas und die Akklimatisierungsprozesse in grosser Höhe. Ergebn. inn. Med. u. Kinderheilk. **54**, 585–671.

Kitchel, R. L., and W. M. Hoskins. (1935.) Respiratory ventilation in the cockroach in air, in carbon dioxide and in nicotine atmospheres. J. Econ. Entom. **28**, 924–933.

Koch, H. (1934.) Aandeel van bepaalde organen aan de zuurstofopname door het gesloten tracheeënsysteem, bij de larven der Odonata Zygoptera. Naturwetensch. Tijdschr. **16**, 75–80.

Koch, H. (1936.) Recherches sur la physiologie du système trachéen clos. Mém. Acad. Roy. Belg. Cl. Sc. **16**, 1–98.

Koch, H. (1938.) The absorption of chloride ions by the anal papillae of diptera larvae. J. exp. Biol. **15**, 152–160.

Kosmin, N. P., W. W. Alpatov, u. M. S. Resnitschenko. (1932.) Zur Kenntnis des Gaswechsels und des Energieverbrauchs der Biene in Beziehung zu deren Aktivität. Z. vergl. Physiol. **17**, 408–422.

Krogh, A. (1904.) On the tension of carbonic acid in natural waters and especially in the sea. Medd. Grønland, **26**, 333–405.

Krogh, A. (1904.) On the cutaneous and pulmonary respiration of the frog. Skand. Arch. Physiol. **15**, 328–419

Krogh, A. (1904.) Some experiments on the cutaneous respiration of vertebrate animals. Skand. Arch. Physiol. **16**, 348–357.

Krogh, A. (1913.) On the composition of the air in the tracheal system of some insects. Skand. Arch. Physiol. **29**, 29–36.

158   RESPIRATORY MECHANISMS

Krogh, A. (1914.) The quantitative relation between temperature and standard metabolism in animals. Int. Z. physik.-chem. Biol. **1**, 491–508.

Krogh, A. (1919.) The composition of the atmosphere. K. Danske Vid. Selsk. Math. fys. Medd. **1**, 3–19.

Krogh, A. (1919.) The rate of diffusion of gases through animal tissues, with some remarks on the coefficient of invasion. J. Physiol. **52**, 391–408.

Krogh, A. (1920.) Studien über Tracheenrespiration. II. Ueber Gasdiffusion in den Tracheen. III. Die Kombination von mechanischer Ventilation mit Gasdiffusion nach Versuchen an Dytiscuslarven. Pfl. Arch. **179**, 95–112, 113–120.

Krogh, A. (1929.) The anatomy and physiology of capillaries. Revised Edition. New Haven.

Krogh, A., and I. Leitch. (1919.) The respiratory function of the blood in fishes. J. Physiol. **52**, 288–300.

Krogh, A., and J. Lindhard. (1913.) The regulation of respiration and circulation during the initial stages of muscular work. J. Physiol. **47**, 112–136.

Krogh, A., and J. Lindhard. (1920.) The changes in respiration at the transition from work to rest. J. Physiol. **53**, 431–439.

Krogh, A., and H. H. Ussing. (1937.) A note on the permeability of trout eggs to D_2O and H_2O. J. exp. Biol. **14**, 35–37.

Krogh, A., and Zeuthen, E. (1940.) The mechanisms of flight preparation in some insects. J. exp. Biol.

Krogh, Marie. (1915.) The diffusion of gases through the lungs of man. J. Physiol. **49**, 271–300.

Kryzanovsky, S. G. (1934.) Die Atmungsorgane der Fischlarven. Zool. J. Abt. Anat. **58**, 21–60.

Kuster, K. (1933.) A study of the general biology, morphology of the respiratory system, and respiration of. certain aquatic Stratiomyia and Odontomyia larvae (Diptera). Michigan Acad. Sc. **19**, 605–658.

Lamy, É. (1902.) Recherches anatomiques sur les trachées des Araignées. Ann. Sc. Nat. Zool. VIII. **15**, 149–280.

Lankester, E. R. (1872.) A contribution to the knowledge of hæmoglobin. Proc. Roy. Soc. **21**, 70–81.

Laurie, A. H. (1933.) Some aspects of respiration in blue and fin whales. Discovery Rep. **7**, 363–406.

Lee, M. O. (1925.) On the mechanism of respiration in certain Orthoptera. J. Exp. Zool. **41**, 125–154.

Lee, M. O. (1929.) Respiration in the insects. Quart. Rev. Biol. **4**, 213–232.

Leiner, M. (1938.) Die Physiologie der Fischatmung. Leipzig. 1–134.

Leitch, Isabella. (1916.) The function of hæmoglobin in invertebrates with special reference to Planorbis and Chironomus larvæ. J. Physiol. **50**, 370–379.

Liljestrand, G. (1918.) Untersuchungen über die Atmungsarbeit. Skand. Arch. Physiol. **35**, 199–293.

Lindhard, J. (1920.) Untersuchungen über statische Muskelarbeit. Skand. Arch. Physiol. **40**, 145–195.

Lindroth, A. (1938.) Atmungsregulation bei Astacus fluviatilis. Arkiv f. Zool. **30 B**, No. 3, 1–7.

Lindroth, A. (1938.) Gibt es bei den Polychäten intestinale Atmung per anum? Z. vergl. Physiol. **25**, 283–292.

Lindroth, A. (1938.) Studien über die respiratorischen Mechanismen von Nereis virens Sars. Zool. Bidrag Uppsala, **17**, 367–497.

Lindroth, A. (1939.) Beobachtungen an Capitelliden, besonders hinsichtlich ihrer Respiration. Zool. Anz. **127**, 285–297.

Lüdicke, M. (1936.) Ueber die Atmung von Emys orbicularis L. Zool. Jb. Abt. Allg. Zool. **56**, 83–106.

Maas, J. A. (1939.) Ueber die Atmung von Helix pomatia L. Z. vergl. Physiol. **26**, 605–610.

McArthur, J. M. (1929.) An experimental study of the functions of the different spiracles in certain Orthoptera. J. exp. Zoöl. **53**, 117–128.

McGovran, E. R. (1931.) A method of measuring tracheal ventilation in insects and some results obtained with grasshoppers. Ann. Ent. Soc. Amer. **24**, 751–761.

Maloeuf, N. S. R. (1938.) The basis of the rhythmic flashing of the firefly. Ann. Ent. Soc. Amer. **31**, 374–380.

Maluf, N. S. R. (1939.) The blood of Arthropods. Quart. Rev. Biol. **14**, 149–191.

Marey, E. J. (1890.) Le Vol des Oiseaux. Paris.

Meldrum, N. U., and F. I. W. Roughton. (1933.) Carbonic Anhydrase. Its preparation and properties. The state of carbon dioxide in blood. J. Physiol. **80**, 113–142.

Mellanby, K. (1935.) The structure and function of the spiracles of the tick, Ornithodoros moubata Murray. Parasitology, **27**, 288–290.

Mellanby, K. (1935.) The evaporation of water from insects. Biol. Rev. **10**, 317–333.

Meyer, Helga. (1935.) Die Atmung von Uranoscopus scaber und ihre Abhängigkeit vom Sauerstoffdruck. Z. vergl. Physiol. **22**, 435–449.

Morgan, A. H., and Grierson, M. C. (1932.) The functions of the gills in burrowing mayflies (Hexagenia recurvata). Physiol. Zool. **5**, 230–245.

Morgan, Ann H., and Helen D. O'Neill. (1931.) The function of the tracheal gills in larvae of the caddis fly, Macronema zebratum Hagen. Physiol. Zoöl. **4**, 361–379.

Nielsen, E. T. (1935.) Ueber den Stoffwechsel der von Grabwespen paralysierten Tiere. Vid. Medd. Dansk Naturh. Forening, **99**, 149–231.

Nielsen, M. (1936.) Die Respirationsarbeit bei Körperruhe und bei Muskelarbeit. Skand. Arch. Physiol. **74**, 299–315.

Nielsen, M. (1936.) Untersuchungen über die Atemregulation beim Menschen besonders mit Hinblick auf die Art des chemischen Reizes. Skand. Arch. Physiol. Suppl. Nr. 10, **74**, 87–208.

Nielsen, M. (1938.) Die Regulation der Körpertemperatur bei Muskelarbeit. Skand. Arch. Physiol. **79**, 193–230.

Nielsen, M., unter Mitarbeit von E. Fridrichsen. (1938.) Eine Modifikation des Krogh'schen Fahrradergometers. Skand. Arch. Physiol. **78**, 76–82.

Nielsen, M., u. O. Hansen. (1937.) Maximale körperliche Arbeit bei Atmung O_2-reicher Luft. Skand. Arch. Physiol. **76**, 37–59.

Olthof, H. J. (1935.) Die Kohlensäure als Atemreiz bei Wassertieren, insbesondere bei Süsswasserfischen. Z. vergl. Physiol. **21**, 534–544.

Pantin, C. F. A. (1932.) Physiological adaptation. J. Linn. Soc. Zool. **37**, 705–711.

Parhon, Marie. (1909.) Les échanges nutritifs chez les abeilles pendant les quatres saisons. Ann. Sc. natur. **9**, 1–58.

Pause, J. (1918.) Beiträge zur Biologie und Physiologie der Larve von Chironomus gregarius. Zool. Jb. Abt. allg. Zool. **36**, 339–452.

Peters, F. (1938.) Ueber die Regulation der Atembewegungen des Flusskrebses Astacus fluviatilis Fabr. Z. vergl. Physiol. **25**, 591–611.

Pflüger, E. (1872.) Ueber die Diffusion des Sauerstoffs, den Ort und die Gesetze der Oxydationsprocesse im thierischen Organismus. Pfl. Arch. **6**, 43–64.

Piéron, H. (1908). De l'influence de l'oxygène dissous sur le comportement des invertébrés marins. II. Quelques moyens de défense contre l'asphyxie. C. R. Soc. Biol. **64**, 955–957.

Plate, L. H. (1898.) Beiträge zur Anatomie und Systematik der Janelliden (Janella schauinslandi n. sp. und Aneitella berghi n. sp.). Zool. Jb. Abt. Anat. **11**, 193–280.

Plateau, F. (1887.) De l'absence de mouvements respiratoires perceptibles chez les Arachnides. Arch. Biol. **7**, 331–348.

Poisson, R. (1926.) L'Anisops producta Fieb. (Hémiptère Notonectidæ). Observations sur son anatomie et sa biologie. (Arch. Zool. exp. gén. **65**, 181–208.

Portier, P. (1911.) Recherches physiologiques sur les insectes aquatiques. Arch. zool. exp. gén. V, **8**, 89–379.

Portier, P. (1933.) Locomotion aérienne et respiration des lépidoptères, un nouveau rôle physiologique des ailes et des écailles. Trav. V. Congr. intern. Ent. Paris. **2**, 25–31.

Portier, P., et M. Duval. (1929.) Recherches sur la teneur en gaz carbonique de l'atmosphère interne des fourmilieres. C. R. Soc. Biol. **102**, 906–908.

Potter, G. E. (1927.) Respiratory function of the swim bladder in Lepidosteus. J. exp. Zool. **49**, 45–67.

Precht, H. (1939.) Die Lungenatmung der Süsswasserpulmonaten. Z. vergl. Physiol. **26**, 696–739.

Prenant, A. (1900.) Notes cytologiques. Cellules trachéales des oestres. Arch. d'anat. micr. **3**, 292–336.

Pulikovsky, Nadine. (1927.) Die respiratorischen Anpassungserscheinungen bei den Puppen der Simuliiden. Z. Wiss. Biol. A. **7**, 384–443.

Pütter, A. (1909.) Die Ernährung des Wassertiere. Jena.

Raffy, Anne. (1935.) Physiologie des Amphibes. L'intensité respiratoire de quelques Crabes de differents niveaux en milieu aérien et aquatique. Bull. de l'Inst. Océanogr. Nr. 662, 1–4.

162 RESPIRATORY MECHANISMS

Raffy, Anne, et P. Portier. (1931.) Intensité des echanges respiratoires pendant le vol chez les Lépidoptères. C. R. Soc. Biol. **108**, 1062–1064.

Redfield, A. C. (1933.) The evolution of the respiratory function of the blood. Quart. Rev. Biol. **8**, 31–57.

Redfield, A. C., T. Coolidge, and A. L. Hurd. (1926.) The transport of oxygen and carbon dioxide by some bloods containing hemocyanin. J. Biol. Chem. **69**, 475–509.

Redfield, A. C., and M. Florkin. (1931.) The respiratory function of the blood of Urechis caupo. Biol. Bull. **61**, 185–210.

Redfield, A. C., and Elisabeth N. Ingalls. (1933.) The oxygen dissociation curves of some bloods containing hemocyanin. J. cell. a. comp. Physiol. **3**, 169–202.

Richet, C. (1899.) De la résistance des canards à l'asphyxie. J. Physiol. et Path. gén. **1**, 641–650.

Riess, J. A. (1881.) Der Bau der Kiemenblätter bei den Knochenfischen. Arch. f. Naturgesch. **47**, 518–550.

Robertson, K., and J. K. W. Ferguson. (1936.) The distribution of carbonic anhydrase in some invertebrates. Amer. J. Physiol. **116**, 130–131.

Root, R. W. (1931.) The respiratory function of the blood of marine fishes. Biol. Bull. **61**, 427–456.

Roughton, F. I. W. (1935.) Recent work on carbon dioxide transport by the blood. Physiol. Rev. **15**, 241–296.

Rubner, M. (1883.) Ueber den Einfluss der Körpergrösse auf Stoff- und Kraftwechsel. Z. Biol. **19**, 536–562.

Saalfeld, E. v. (1936.) Untersuchungen über das Hacheln bei Tauben. Z. vergl. Physiol. **23**, 727–743.

Saalfeld, E. v. (1938.) Untersuchungen der Fledermaus-Atmung. Z. vergl. Physiol. **26**, 242–252.

Scharnke, H. (1938.) Experimentelle Beiträge zur Kenntnis der Vogelatmung. Z. vergl. Physiol. **25**, 548–583.

Scholander, P. F. (1940.) Experimental investigations on the respiration in diving mammals and birds. Hvalraadets Skr. Nr. **22**, Norske Vid. Akad. 1–131.

Schulze, F. E. (1912.) Ueber die Luftsäcke der Vögel. Verh. d. VIII. intern. Zool. Kongr. Graz 1910, 446–482.

Schöttle, Elfriede. (1932.) Morphologie und Physiologie der Atmung bei wasser- schlamm- und landlebenden Gobiiformes. Z. wiss. Zool. **140**, 1–114.

Scott, W. J. (1938.) Gas transport by the blood of the opossum, Didelphys virginiana. J. cell. a. comp. Physiol. **12**, 391–401.

Semper, C. (1878.) Ueber die Lunge von Birgus latro. Z. wiss. Zool. **30**, 282–287.

Soum, M. (1896.) Recherches physiologiques sur l'appareil respiratoire des oiseaux. These Lyon.

Spärck, R. (1936.) On the relation between metabolism and temperature in some marine lamellibranches, and its zoogeographical significance. K. Danske Vid. Selsk. Biol. Medd. **13**, 3–27.

Stahn, Ingeborg. (1928.) Ueber die Atmungsregulation, besonders die Kohlensäureregulation, bei Dixippus morosus und Aeschna grandis. Zool. Jb., Abt. allg. Zool. **46**, 1–86.

Stephenson, J. (1912/14.) On intestinal respiration in Annelids. Trans. Roy. Soc. Edinb. **49**, 735–829.

Stoller, J. H. (1899.) On the organs of respiration of the Oniscidae. Zoologica, **10**, 1–31.

Svedberg, T. (1933.) Sedimentation constants, molecular weights and isoelectric points of the respiratory proteins. J. Biol. Chem. **103**, 311–325.

Theorell, H. (1934.) Kristallinisches Myoglobin. V. Die Sauerstoffbindungskurve des Myoglobins. Biochem. Z. **268**, 73–82.

Thompson, Th. G., B. D. Thomas, and C. A. Barnes. (1934.) Distribution of dissolved oxygen in the North Pacific Ocean. James Johnstone Memorial Volume. 203–234.

Thorpe, W. H. (1932.) Experiments upon respiration in the larvæ of certain parasitic Hymenoptera. Proc. Roy. Soc. B. **109**, 450–471.

Varley, G. C. (1937.) Aquatic insect larvae which obtain oxygen from the roots of plants. Proc. Ent. Soc. London **12**, 55–60.

Verhoeff, K. W. (1921.) Ueber die Atmung der Landasseln, zugleich ein Beitrag zur Kenntnis der Entstehung der Landtiere. Z. wiss. Zool. **118**, 365–446.

Volsøe, H. (1939.) The sea snakes of the Iranian Gulf and the Gulf of Oman. With a summary of the biology of the sea snakes. Danish Sc. Inv. in Iran, I, 9–45.

Vos, H. J. (1934.) Ueber den Weg der Atemluft in der Entenlunge. Z. vergl. Physiol. **21**, 552–578.

Vos, H. J. (1936.) Over Ademhaling En Reukzin Bij Reptielen En Amphibiën. Proefschrift. Groningen.

Vos, H. J.   (1937.)   Ueber das Fehlen der rekurrenten Bronchien beim Pinguin und bei den Reptilien.   Zool. Anz. **117**, 176–181.

Wallengren, H.   (1914.)   Physiolog.-Biolog. Studien über die Atmung bei den Arthropoden III.   Die Atmung der Aeschnalarven.   Lunds Univ. Aarsskr. N. F. Avd. 2, **10**, No. 8, 1–28.

Walter, Elfriede.   (1922.)   Beiträge zur Kenntnis der Larven von Hypoderma und Gastrus.   Zool. Jb. Abt. Syst. **45**, 587–608.

Wastl, H., u. G. Leiner.   (1931.)   Beobachtungen über die Blutgase bei Vögeln. I. II. III.   Pfl. Arch. **227**, 367–474.

Westerlund, A.   (1906.)   Studien über die Athembewegungen der Karausche mit besonderer Rücksicht auf den verschiedenen Gasgehalt des Athemwassers.   Skand. Arch. Physiol. **18**, 263–280.

Wigglesworth, V. B.   (1929.)   A theory of tracheal respiration in insects.   Nature, **124**, 986.

Wigglesworth, V. B.   (1930.)   A theory of tracheal respiration in insects.   Proc. Roy. Soc. B, **106**, 230–250.

Wigglesworth, V. B.   (1931.)   The extent of air in the tracheoles of some terrestrial insects.   Proc. Roy. Soc. B, **109**, 354–359.

Wigglesworth, V. B.   (1931.)   The respiration of insects.   Biol. Rev. **6**, 181–220.

Wigglesworth, V. B.   (1935.)   The regulation of respiration in the flea, *Xenopsylla Cheopis*, Roths. (Pulicidae).   Proc. Roy. Soc. B, **118**, 397–419.

Wigglesworth, V. B.   (1939.)   The principles of insect physiology.   London.

Willmer, E. N.   (1934.)   Some observation on the respiration of certain tropical fresh-water fishes.   J. exp. Biol. **11**, 283–306.

Winterstein, H.   (1908.)   Beiträge zur Kenntnis der Fischatmung.   Pfl. Arch. **125**, 73–98.

Winterstein, H.   (1909.)   Zur Kenntnis der Blutgase wirbelloser Seetiere.   Biochem. Z. **19**, 384–424.

Winterstein, H.   (1911.)   Die Regulierung der Atmung durch das Blut.   Pfl. Arch. **138**, 167–184.

Winterstein, H.   (1912.)   Die physikalisch-chemischen Erscheinungen der Atmung.   Handb. vergl. Physiol. **1**, 1–264.

Winterstein, H.   (1921.)   Die Reaktionstheorie der Atmungsregulation.   Pfl. Arch. **187**, 293–298.

Winterstein, H.   (1925.)   Ueber die chemische Regulierung der Atmung bei den Cephalopoden.   Z. vergl. Physiol. **2**, 315–328.

Wit, F. (1932.) Ueber den Einfluss der Luftfeuchtigkeit auf die Grösse der Atemöffnung bei Landpulmonaten. Z. vergl. Physiol. **18**, 116–124.

Wolf, S. (1933.) Zur Kenntnis von Bau und Funktion der Reptilienlunge. Zool. Jb. Abt. Anat. **57**, 139–190.

Wolvekamp, H. P. (1932.) Untersuchungen über den Sauerstofftransport durch Blutpigmente bei Helix, Rana und Planorbis. Z. vergl. Physiol. **16**, 1–38.

Wolvekamp, H. P. (1938.) Ueber den Sauerstofftransport durch Hämocyanin von Octopus vulgaris Lam. und Sepia officinalis L. Z. vergl. Physiol. **25**, 541–547.

Ysseling, M. A. (1930.) Ueber die Atmung der Weinbergschnecke (Helix pomatia). Z. vergl. Physiol. **13**, 1–60.

Zimmer, K. (1935.) Beiträge zur Mechanik der Atmung bei den Vögeln in Stand und Flug. Zoologica **33**, 1–69.

Zoond, A. (1931.) Studies in the localisation of respiratory exchange in invertebrates. II. The branchial filaments of the sabellid, Bispira voluticornis. J. exp. Biol. **8**, 258–262.

Zoond, A. (1931.) Studies in the localisation of respiratory exchange in invertebrates. III. The book lungs of the scorpion. J. exp. Biol. **8**, 263–266.

Zoond, A., and Enid Charles. (1931.) Studies in the localisation of respiratory exchange in invertebrates. I. The respiratory mechanism of the fresh-water crab Potamonautes. J. exp. Biol. **8**, 250–257.

LIST OF ANIMALS

and the Pages on which Their Respiratory Mechanisms
Are Mentioned

LIST OF ANIMALS

INDEX

Absorption coefficients for gases, 11
Air-sacs, 63, 71ff., 126, 127
Air stores, gill function of, 134ff.
Anaërobiosis, 8

Blood, 88ff.
—, dissociation curves, 95ff., 110
—, — —, adaptation to high altitudes, 100ff.
—, — —, fœtal, 99
—, — —, in variable environments, 102ff.
—, oxygen capacity of, 79, 81, 94, 95, 110, 111, 112
—, supply of respiratory organs, 42, 50, 51
—, transport capacity for CO_2, 89ff., 114
—, — — — O_2, 93ff., 112
Branchial respiration, *see* Gills

Caisson disease, 85ff.
Carbon dioxide in air, 9ff.
— — — waters, 15, 105
— —, action on spiracles, 58
— —, — — respiratory movements, 65, 131
— —, convection transport, 88ff., 114
— —, diffusion transport, 20
— —, dissociation curves in blood, 90–91
— —, influence on O_2-affinity of blood, 96ff., 105
— —, insensitivity to CO_2 in divers, 61, 81
— —, tension in water, 16, 106, 143
Carbon monoxide, diffusion in lungs, 19, 64, 67
— —, hæmoglobin, 103–104
Carbonic anhydrase, 92–93
Chlorocruorin, 93, 111
Circulation rate, in divers, 84
— —, at high altitudes, 101
— —, during work, 113
Counter-current flow, 39

Cutaneous respiration, 21ff., 53, 140
— —, accessory, 54, 79

Dead space of air passages, 75, 86, 87
— — in tracheæ, 128
Diffusion coefficients, 18, 20
—, lungs, 55ff.
—, respiration, 18, 21ff., 53
Diving, 78ff.
—, behaviour of animals in, 81
Dyspnœa, 37, 60, 74

Evaporation regulation, 52, 59, 76, 120–121

Flight preparation (in insects), 129
—, respiration during, 77, 129ff.

Gas tensions, definition, 12
— —, of CO_2 in water, 16, 106, 143
— —, loading and unloading, 96ff.
— —, relations of, to quantities, 88
Gills, 31ff.
—, definition, 27
—, for air breathing, 44, 46ff., 54, 143
—, in cavity, 34ff.
—, influence of O_2 concentration on development of, 33
—, surface measurements, 42, 140
—, respiration regulation in, 42, 106
—, tracheal, 139ff.
—, ventilation cost, 41
—, — coupled to locomotion, 38, 140
—, — mechanisms, 35ff.

Heat regulation, 66, 76, 78
— —, during work, 7
Hæmerythrin, 93, 111
Hæmocyanin, 93, 109ff.
Hæmoglobin, 93ff.
—, in muscles, 81, 102, 106
—, oxygen affinity of, 30
—, as oxygen store, 106ff.

171